11+ & SATS MATHS

Book Four

Stephen C. Curran

edited by
Anne-Marie Choong
Tandip Singh Mann

This book belongs to:

....

Accelerated Education Publications Ltd.

Contents

Chapter Eleven
PROBABILITY
1. What is Probability?

Probability is a way of measuring the **Likelihood** or **Chance** that a particular thing might happen. This happening is called an **Event** or **Outcome**. Some Probabilities can only be measured in broad terms. An Event that can happen is called a **Possibility**. A Probability can range from **Definite (Certain) right through to Impossible**.

Certain — The sun will rise tomorrow.

↑

Likely — I will have three meals today.

↑

Possible — It will rain tomorrow.

↑

Unlikely — I will win the Lottery Jackpot.

↑

Impossible — I can fly to Mars next week.

Exercise 11: 1 Write if the Event is **Certain**, **Likely**, **Possible**, **Unlikely or Impossible**.

1) All the boys in one year 5 class will support the same football team ....
2) Autumn is followed by winter ....
3) I will have dinner this evening ....
4) I will eat some chips next weekend ....

5) My best friend will phone me within the next 10 days ....

6) I will become a world famous pop star when I grow up ....

7) I will climb Mount Everest in the next hour ....

8) The Earth orbits around the Sun once a year ....

9) I will have tea with the Prime Minister tomorrow ....

Score Out of Ten →

10) I will watch television tomorrow ....

2. Estimating Probability

a. The Probability Scale

All Probabilities have a **Value between 0** and **1**. A Certain Event has a Value of **1**. An Impossible Event has a Value of **0**. An Event with a **50-50 (Even)** chance of occuring lies in the middle. Other Probabilities lie somewhere between **0** and **1**. A Probability scale can show the **Range of Probabilities**.

Evens (50-50) Equal chance

0 ———————— $\frac{1}{2}$ ———————— **1**

Impossible — **Certain**

Example:

A series of items are dropped onto a stone floor. Estimate the Probability of each item breaking and place them on the Probability Scale.

Plastic CD case Tomato China cereal bowl Wine glass Metal knife

0 ———————— **1**

Metal knife (at 0) → **Plastic CD case** → **China cereal bowl** → **Tomato** → **Wine glass**

b. Experimental Techniques

Experiments can be conducted to Estimate the Probability of an Event. Example:

How many children will want a school lunch next week?

The numbers of children taking school lunch could be recorded for some weeks by taking a Survey. From this a Probability of future take up on lunches can be calculated.

c. Theoretical Techniques

If there is a Theoretical answer the Probability can be found without conducting an Experiment. This happens if all the different results have the same Chance of occuring - **All the Probabilities are Equal**. Objects with Equal Probabilities are said to have **Symmetry Characteristics** and are deemed as **'Fair'**. Each **Outcome** is Equally Likely.

Example: What kind of objects have Symmetry Characteristics and are 'Fair'?

Dice

6 Equal shaped sides. An Equal chance of throwing a **1**, **2**, **3**, **4**, **5** or **6**.

A Spinner

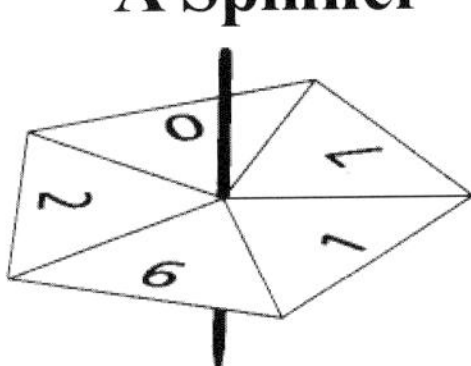

5 Equal shaped sides. Each face is Equally likely to be spun.

A Coin

2 Equal sides. An Equal Chance of tossing a head or a tail.

Playing Cards

52 cards that look identical when face down. Choosing any card is Equally likely.

An object would be **'Unfair'** or **'Biased'** if it did NOT give Equally Likely Outcomes.

Example: These three cards are removed from a pack of cards. Is this a 'Fair' pack?

It is an 'Unfair' or 'Biased' pack because cards cannot be selected on a random basis with Equally Likely Outcomes.

Exercise 11: 2a

Do these have **Symmetry Characteristics**? Write Yes or No.

1) a) An incomplete pack of **39** cards ....

b) A complete pack of **52** playing cards ....

2) a) A spinner with **6** Equal Sides ....

b) A spinner with **8** Unequally shaped sides ....

Write whether the following are '**Fair**' or '**Unfair**'.

3) a) A coin is carefully rolled onto one side, so that heads is the only Possible Outcome ....

b) A coin is tossed so that both heads and tails are Equally Likely Outcomes ....

4) A complete set of **100** raffle tickets ....

5) A die is weighted on one side so that it always lands on a six. The die is thrown and it shows a six ....

3. Events and Outcomes

Event (Two meanings) 1. An **activity** itself or 2. The **result** of the activity.

Outcome (One meaning) The **result** of an activity.

Example: Identify Event and Outcome when a die is rolled.

A die is rolled (**Event**). It lands on a 1, 2, 3, 4, 5, or 6 (**Event** and **Outcome**).

a. Mutually Exclusive Events

These are sets of Events or Outcomes where the occurence of one of them means that none of the others can happen.

Example: A 'one' rolled on a die. Is this a Mutually Exclusive Event?

Yes, this is a Mutually Exclusive Event, because if a 'one' is rolled no other number can be rolled at the same time.

b. Independent Events

Two or more Events or Outcomes are Independent if the happening of one of them has no effect on the other.

Example: Two dice are rolled. One shows a 'two' and the other a 'one'. Are these Events Independent of each other?

Yes, these are Independent Events. The number showing on one die does NOT influence the number on the other die.

c. Dependent Events

Two Events are Dependent if the first Event occurring affects the Probability of a second Event.

Example:

One spinner is numbered **1** to **8** and another is numbered **1** to **6**. One spinner is chosen at random (Event 1) and I spin a **3** (Event 2). Are the Events Dependent?

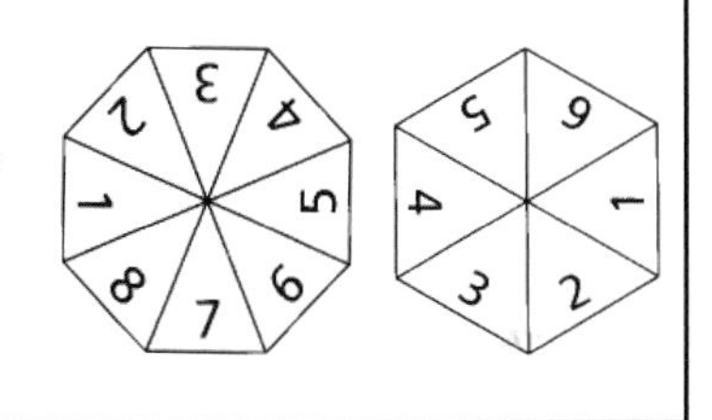

Yes, the Events are Dependent because the Probability of spinning a **3** depends on which of the two spinners was chosen.

Exercise 11: 2b Write 'Yes' or 'No' to the following:

6) A **1p** coin is tossed and it lands on tails. Is this a Mutually Exclusive Event? ....

7) Two spinners both numbering **1 to 6** are spun. One shows a **6** and the other a **4**. Are the Events Independent? ....

8) Two coins are tossed. They both show heads. Are the Events Independent? ....

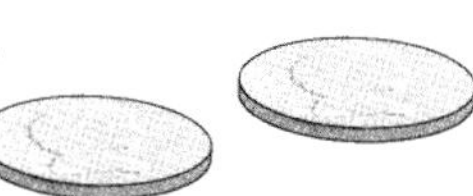

9) I have two die. I roll a **4** with one of them. Is the score I roll on the second die and the sum of the two scores Independent? ....

10) Two bags hold different numbers of black and white balls as shown. One bag is chosen at random (Event 1) and a single black ball is randomly drawn out (Event 2).

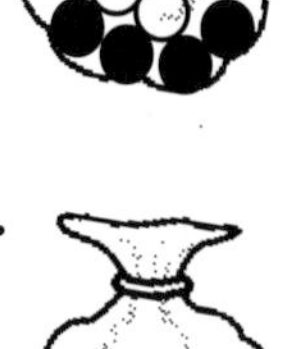

a) Are the two Events Dependent? ....
b) Are the two Events Independent? ....

Score

4. Possible Outcomes

a. The Set of All Possible Outcomes

If there are a number of Definite (Certain) **Outcomes** or **Possibilities** for an Event occuring they are termed as the **Set of all Possible Outcomes** or **Exhaustive Events**.

Example: What are all the Possible Outcomes if a 'Fair' die is thrown.

A **Fair** die (thrown fairly) will only give six possible scores. **1, 2, 3, 4, 5** or **6** - This is the **Set of all Possible Outcomes**. One object (die) limits the number of Possible Outcomes.

Exercise 11: 3a Write out the Possible Outcomes.

1) Tossing a **50p** coin .... or ....

2) A spinner has six sides. They are numbered from **1** to **6**.
....

3) A box contains four different coloured balls: green, red, blue and yellow. Each can be drawn at random and replaced. ....

4) In a pack of cards there are four suits; hearts, diamonds, spades and clubs. In terms of suits of cards the Possible Outcomes are: ....

b. Representing Possible Outcomes

If there is more than one Object used then it increases the number of Possible Outcomes. Information with Symmetry characteristics can be represented in three different ways:

Lists **Tables** **Sample Space Diagrams**

(i). Lists (of Possible Outcomes)

This involves making a List of all the Possible Outcomes. It is a suitable method when a small number of Outcomes need to be recorded. Example:

List all the Possible Outcomes if two 'Fair' coins are tossed?

4 combinations are possible:

H H
T T
H T
T H

This is really **3** rather than **4 Possible Outcomes** (HT is interchangeable with TH). The List can be vertical or horizontal. **HH TT HT**

Exercise 11: 3b List the Possible Outcomes.

5) A small box contains three balls of different colours: Black, White and Grey. A ball is drawn out at random and then put back. The box is shaken and another ball is drawn out.

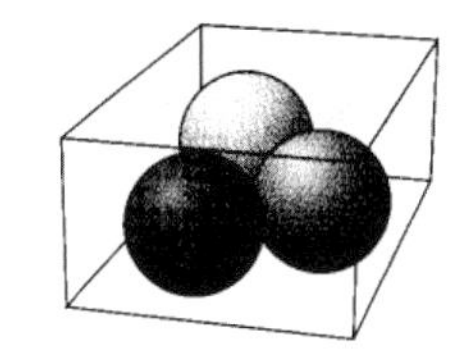

List the **9** Possible Outcomes ....
....

6) Alan (A), Ben (B), Carol (C) and Denise (D) organise a tennis league. They put their names in a hat and draw out two names replacing them each time. They draw out all the Possible combinations (The order in which the names are drawn out does not matter). List the **6** Possible Outcomes.

....

(ii). Tables (of Possible Outcomes)

When there are more Possible Outcomes it can be easier to create a Table.

Example:

Record on a Table all the Possible Outcomes if three coins are tossed on a repeated basis.

1st Coin	2nd Coin	3rd Coin
H	H	H
H	H	T
H	T	H
T	H	H
H	T	T
T	H	T
T	T	H
T	T	T

There are **8 Possible Outcomes** for the three coins.

Exercise 11: 3c Tabulate the Possible Outcomes.

7) If these two spinners were spun repeatedly there would be **9** Possible Outcomes. Write these on the Table.

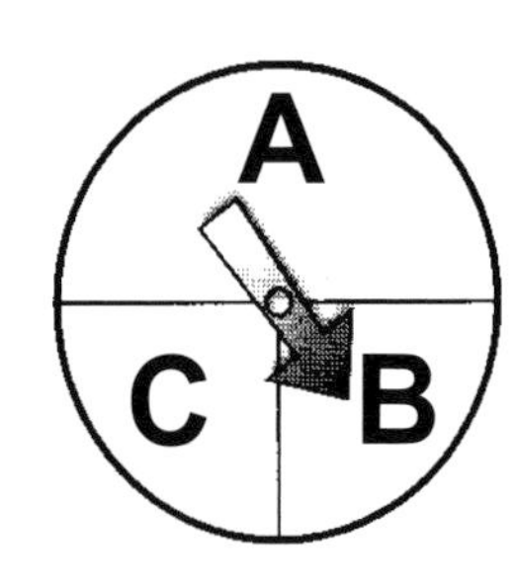

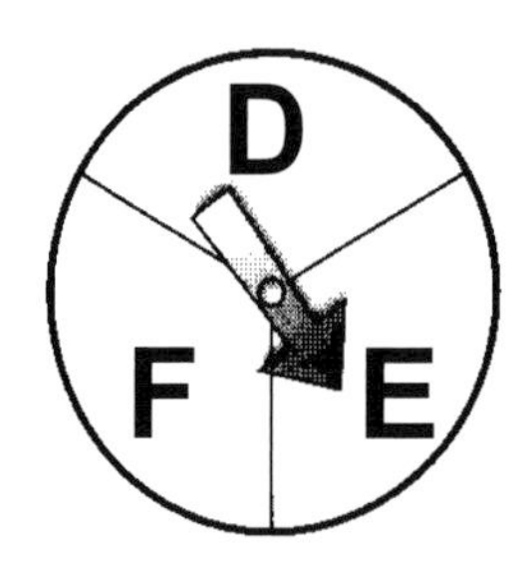

Spinner 1	Spinner 2

8) Paul (P), Rikesh (R), Surjeet (S) and Thomas (T) wrote their names on paper and put them in a hat. They repeatedly drew out two names at random and replaced them each time. Record the six Possible Outcomes on the Table.

Name 1	Name 2

(iii). Sample Space Diagrams (of Possible Outcomes)

A Sample Space Diagram can be drawn to represent Possible Outcomes. Each cross marks an Outcome.

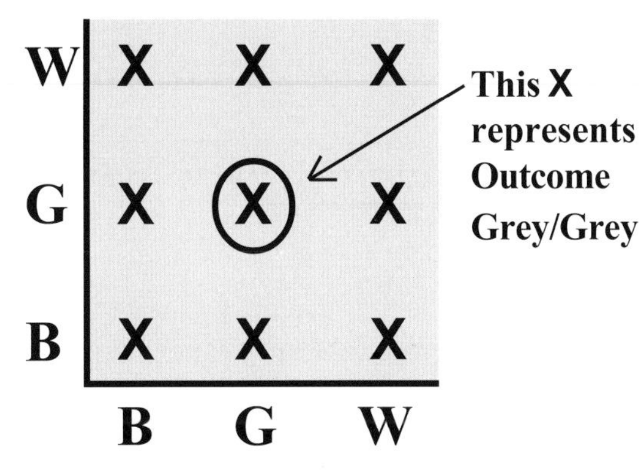

The **9 Possible Outcomes** can be Listed. Eg. BB, BG.

Example 1:

A bag contains three balls of different colours: Black, White and Grey. A ball is drawn out at random and then put back. The bag is shaken and another ball is drawn out. Record all the Possible Outcomes on a Sample Space Diagram.

When the number of Possible Outcomes are too large to record by Listing or on a Table, a Sample Space Diagram should be drawn.

6	7	8	9	10	11	12
5	6	7	8	9	10	11
4	5	6	7	8	9	10
3	4	5	6	7	8	9
2	3	4	5	6	7	8
1	2	3	4	5	6	7
	1	**2**	**3**	**4**	**5**	**6**

Example 2:

Two dice are thrown until all the Possible Outcomes are Exhausted. Record all the Possible Outcomes on a Sample Space Diagram.

There are **36 Possible Outcomes** which could be Listed. The Sample Space Diagram records them as **Scores**. They could be represented by **X** as before. They are all Mutually Exclusive, Independent and Equally Likely Events.

Exercise 11: 3d Answer the following questions:

9a) A die and a coin are thrown. List the Possible Outcomes from the Diagram.

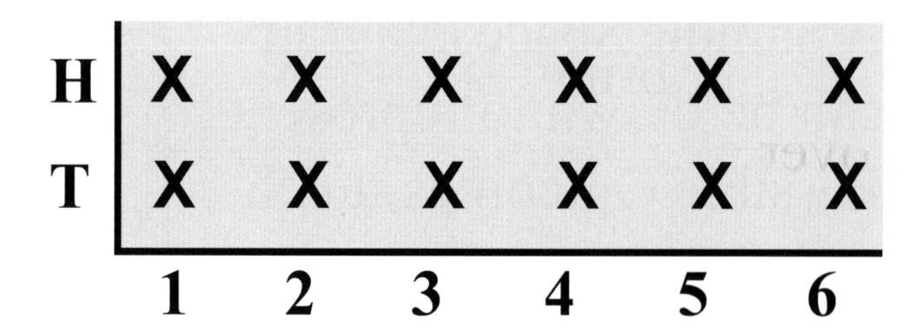

....

....

9b) A six sided and an eight sided spinner are spun until all the Possible Outcomes are Exhausted. Fill in all the Possible Outcomes (Scores) on the Diagram (one line is done).

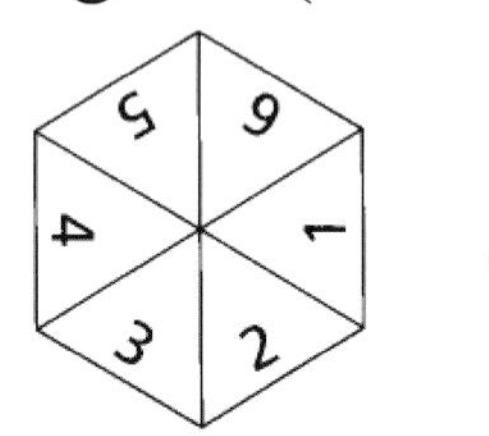

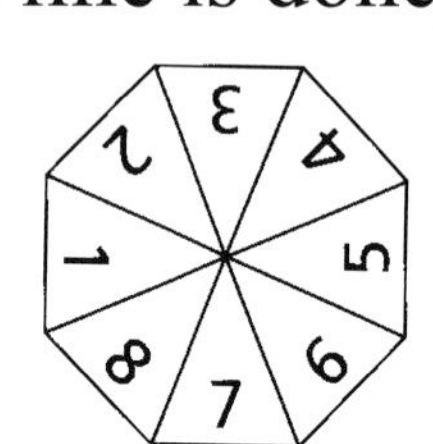

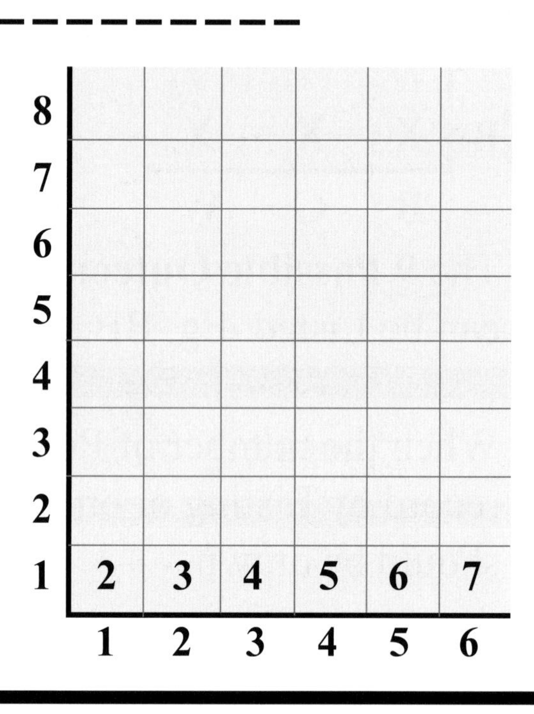

Probabilities can be worked out from Survey information which has no Symmetry Characteristics and where Theoretical Techniques do not apply. Possible Outcomes are usually recorded using the following:

Sample Tree Diagrams **Two-Way Tables**

(iv). Sample Tree Diagrams (of Possible Outcomes)

In Sample Tree Diagrams Probabilities are written on Branches in Decimal or Fraction form.
Each Set of Possible Outcomes adds to 1.

Example:

Record the Survey of a year 6 class having a school lunch (**SL**) or bringing their own packed lunch (**PL**) to school over a two day period. What were the Outcomes on day two of the class Survey?

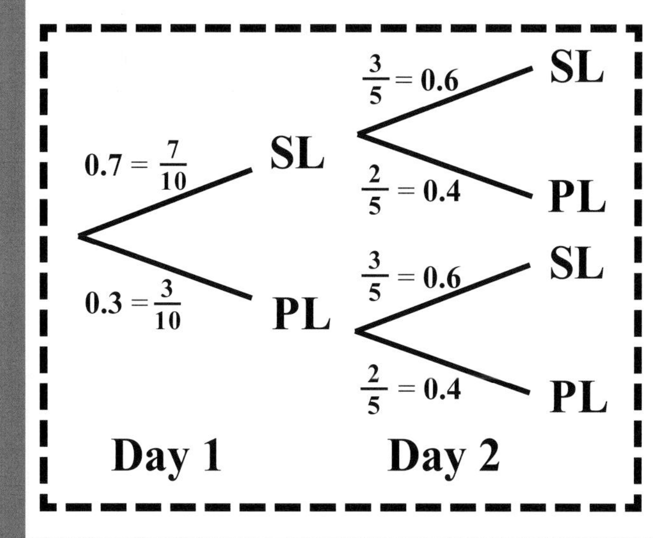

This Sample Tree Diagram shows that on **day 2** of the Survey:

$\mathbf{0.6} = \frac{6}{10} = \frac{3}{5}$ of the class chose a school lunch.

$\mathbf{0.4} = \frac{4}{10} = \frac{2}{5}$ of the class chose a packed lunch.

(v). Two-Way Tables (of Possible Outcomes)

A Two-Way Table records the Possible Outcomes in detail.

Example:

Record the same Survey about whether a year 6 class choose a school lunch or a packed lunch on a Two-Way Table. What were the Outcomes on day two of the Survey?

A Two-Way Table can record the same information in a detailed way.

Lunch Choice	Day 1	Day 2	Total
School Lunch	21	18	39
Packed Lunch	9	12	21
Total	30	30	60

On day two of the Survey the children chose the following:

$\frac{\not{18}^{3}}{\not{30}_{5}} = \frac{3}{5} = 0.6$ School Lunch

$\frac{\not{12}^{2}}{\not{30}_{5}} = \frac{2}{5} = 0.4$ Packed Lunch

Exercise 11: 3e Answer the following questions:

A Sample Tree Diagram and Two-Way Table is used to show the library choices a year 5 class makes between reference books (**RB**) and story books (**SB**) over two reading sessions.

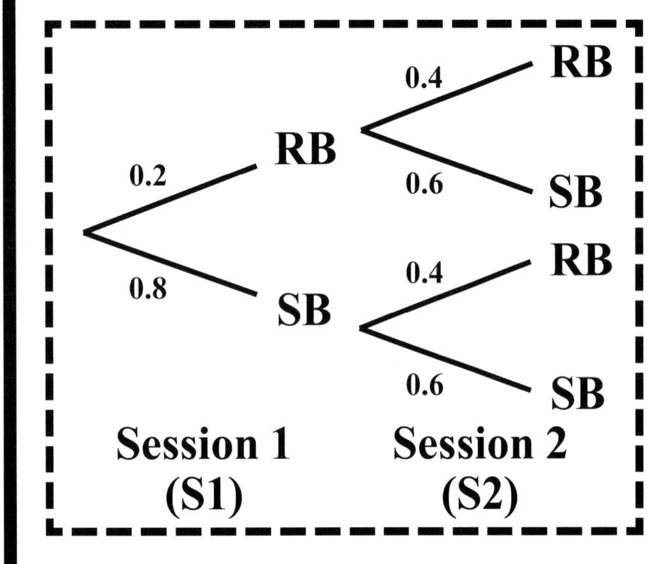

10a) What Proportion of children chose story books in the first session? Write as a Percentage, a Decimal and a Fraction.

.... % ....

10b) $\frac{2}{5}$ of the children chose reference books in session 2. How many children was this? ....

Book Choice	S1	S2	Total
Reference Bks	6	12	18
Story Bks	24	18	42
Total	30	30	60

Score

5. Expressing Probability

a. Equal Probabilities

Probabilities can be predicted from the Fraction:

$$P(\ ) = \frac{\textbf{Number of Favourable Outcomes}}{\textbf{Total Number of Possible Outcomes}}$$

P or ***Pr*** is the symbol for Probability. The brackets **( )** contain the **Outcome/Event**. The Formula can be used with all Objects that have **Symmetry Characteristics**.

Example 1:

Write the Probability of tossing Heads on a coin as a Fraction?

$$P(\text{Head}) = \frac{1}{2}$$

If there is more than one **Favourable Outcome** the Probability can sometimes be **Simplified** as in a Complex Fraction.

Example 2:

What is the Probability of throwing an Odd number when rolling a die?

1, **3** and **5** are odd (3 out of 6)

$$P(\text{Odd}) = \frac{\cancel{3}^{\,1}}{\cancel{6}_{\,2}} \overset{\text{Simplify}}{=} \frac{1}{2} \text{ Chance}$$

The **Chance of throwing an Odd Number** on the die can be expressed in other ways: e.g. As a **1 in 2** (Even) Chance, or as a **Percentage**; **50%**, or as a **Decimal**; **0.5**

Exercise 11: 4a Work out the following:

1) What is the Probability of choosing a blue crayon from a set containing **10** different coloured crayons?

   ***P* (Blue)** = ... A .... Chance.

2) If you buy **15** raffle tickets out of a total of **100**. What is the Chance of winning first prize?

   ***P* (First Prize)** = $\frac{15}{100}$ (Simplify) .... A .... Chance.

3) One card is chosen from a pack of **52** playing cards (there are four suits; each of 13 cards). What is the Probability it is a Diamond? (Complete Fraction and Simplify)

   ***P* (Diamond)** = $\frac{\quad}{52}$ = ... A .... Chance.

b. The Sum of Probabilities

All Probabilities have a **Value between 0** and **1** and can be Expressed as **Decimals**, **Fractions**, **Percentages** or **Ratios**. This can be shown on the Probability Scale.

Impossible	Unlikely	Possible	Likely	Certain
0	**0.25**	**0.5**	**0.75**	**1**
0	$\frac{1}{4}$ **(1 in 4)**	$\frac{1}{2}$ **(Evens or 50/50)**	$\frac{3}{4}$ **(3 in 4)**	**1**
0	**25%**	**50%**	**75%**	**100%**

This also means that the Probability of all the Possible Outcomes for an Event Add up to **1** (One Whole or 100%). It can be stated as: **The Sum of the Probabilities of all Possible Outcomes of an Event, is Equal to 1**.

The Sum of Probabilites can be demonstrated as follows:

Example 1: A coin is tossed. Show the Sum of the Probabilities is Equal to **1**.

1. The Outcomes. $P(\text{H}) = \frac{1}{2}$ and $P(\text{T}) = \frac{1}{2}$
2. The Sum of all the Probabilities. $P(\text{H}) + P(\text{T}) = \frac{1}{2} + \frac{1}{2} = 1$

Example 2: A die is thrown. Show the Sum of the Probabilities is Equal to **1**.

1. The Outcomes.

$P(1) = \frac{1}{6}$ $P(2) = \frac{1}{6}$ $P(3) = \frac{1}{6}$

$P(4) = \frac{1}{6}$ $P(5) = \frac{1}{6}$ $P(6) = \frac{1}{6}$

2. The Sum of all the Probabilities.

$$P(1) + P(2) + P(3) + P(4) + P(5) + P(6) = \frac{1}{6} \times 6 = 1$$

Exercise 11: 4b Work out the following:

4) There are **18** coloured balls in a bag. There are **3** red balls, **6** green balls and **9** blue balls.
What is the Probability of picking a:

a) Red ball .... b) Green ball .... c) Blue ball ....

d) The ....ball has the greatest Probability of being drawn.

5) A jar holds **six** 50p coins, **eight** 2p coins and **eleven** 20p coins. Write the Probability of choosing:

a) **20p** $P(20)$ = ... b) **50p** $P(50)$ = ...

6) One sweet is picked at random from a bag containing **15** chews, **5** mints and **5** chocolates. What is the Probability that the sweet removed will be:

(Express as **%**)

Cancel $\frac{15}{25} \times \frac{100}{1}$

Do your working out here.

a) A chew .... % b) Not a chew .... %

(Express as **Decimals**)

Cancel $\frac{\cancel{5}^{1}}{\cancel{25}_{5}} = \frac{1}{5}$ ↑ **Divide**

c) A mint A .... d) A chew or chocolate ....

---

7) One card is drawn at random from an ordinary pack of **52** playing cards (there are **13** cards in each suit of clubs, spades, hearts and diamonds).
What is the Probability of drawing:

a) A King .... (Any Suit)

b) A black card .... (Clubs or Spades)

c) A picture card of any suit .... (Jacks, Queens, Kings)

c. The Probability of Events Not Occuring

The Probabilities of all possible outcomes of an Event add up to **1**. If the Probability of an Event occurring is known, it is possible to work out the Probability of this Event **not** occurring. It can be written as:

$$P(\textbf{Event Occurring}) + P(\textbf{Event not Occurring}) = 1$$

So $P(\textbf{Event not Occurring}) = 1 - P(\textbf{Event Occurring})$

Example:

If there is a **1 in 6** chance of a **2** showing on the die then what is the chance of a **2** not showing?

$$\frac{1}{6} + P(\textbf{Event not Occurring}) = 1$$

So $P(\textbf{Event not Occurring}) = 1 - \frac{1}{6} = \frac{5}{6}$

The Probability of **not throwing a 2** is $\frac{5}{6}$

Exercise 11: 4c Work out the following: **Score**

8a) A 'Fair' spinner numbers **1 to 9**. If the chance of showing an odd number is $\frac{5}{9}$, what is the chance of not showing an odd number? ....

b) There are **52** cards in a 'Fair' Pack and **13** cards in each suit. If the cards are dealt at random what is the chance of **not** showing a club card? ....

c) There are **21** coloured balls in a bag. There are **7** blue, **6** green and **8** red balls. If a 'Fair' ball is drawn out, what is the chance of not choosing a red ball? ....

d. Repeating Experiments

When Experiments are performed with Symmetric properties the Theoretical Outcome can be predicted.

Example: If a coin is tossed the chance of getting heads is?

There is a **1 in 2** or $\frac{1}{2}$ Chance of getting heads.

However if the coin is tossed just a few times it is unlikely that exactly half of the Outcomes will be heads and half tails. Suppose the coin is tossed **10 times** the Outcomes might be something like this:

T H H H H T T H H T (6H, 4T)

If the Experiment is repeated numerous times, the **Experimental Result** will grow closer to the **Theoretical Answer**. They can be compared by first calculating the **Relative Frequency**.

e. Relative Frequencies

A **Relative Frequency** for a set of experiments compares the number of times an Event occurred with the total number of trials.

Relative Frequency of an Event:

$$\frac{\textbf{Number of Times the Event Occurred}}{\textbf{Total Number of Trials}}$$

Example:

A 'fair' coin is thrown **75** times and a head comes up **30** times. What is the Relative Frequency of getting a head?

$$\textbf{Relative Frequency} = \frac{30}{75} = \textbf{0.4}$$

The Theoretical Probability is 0.5. The Relative Frequency will grow closer to this as the number of trials is increased (repeated). Eventually they will coincide.

Exercise 11: 4d Answer the following:

Give your answers as Decimals.

9a) A 'fair' die is thrown **500** times. If a **4** comes up **80** times, what is the Relative Frequency? $\frac{80}{500} =$ ....

b) A card is blindly drawn from a pack of **52** cards. The pack is re-shuffled and the process repeated a further **199** times. A picture card is drawn **40** times. What is the Relative Frequency of drawing a picture card? ....

f. Expected Number

Probability can be used to Estimate the Expected Number of times an Event is likely to occur by multiplying the Probability of the desired Event occurring by the number of repetitions. This can only be used as a guideline as the Event may need far more more repetition to achieve the Theoretical Probability.

Example:

A die is thrown **150** times. Approximately how many times is a **4** likely to be thrown?

There are six Possible Outcomes on a die.

$$P(4) = \frac{1}{6} \times 150 = 25$$

Exercise 11: 4e Answer the following: **Score**

10a) The Chance that Paul will gain full marks in a spelling test is **0.6**. Over a year he takes **30** spelling tests. In how many tests would he expect to gain full marks? .... tests.

b) Harry plays darts and hits a bull's eye **30%** of the time. If Harry throws **400** darts, how many times can he expect to hit a bull's eye? .... times.

6. Combined Events

If an Experiment is carried out more than once it is called a **Combined Event** and has a number of **Possible Outcomes**.

Finding the Probabilities for Combined Events where the objects have Symmetry Characteristics involves using:

Lists **Tables** **Sample Space Diagrams.**

Example:

Two dice are thrown until all the Possible Outcomes are Exhausted. What is the Chance of throwing any double?

6	7	8	9	10	11	(12)
5	6	7	8	9	(10)	11
4	5	6	7	(8)	9	10
3	4	5	(6)	7	8	9
2	3	(4)	5	6	7	8
1	(2)	3	4	5	6	7
	1	2	3	4	5	6

There are **36** Possible Outcomes (doubles are circled).

$$P(\text{a double}) = \frac{6}{36} = \frac{1}{6}$$

The Sample Space Diagram records all the Possible Outcomes.

Exercise 11: 5a Work out the following:

A six sided and a seven sided spinner are spun until all the Possible Outcomes are Exhausted.

7	8	9	10	11	12	13
6	7	8	9	10	11	12
5	6	7	8	9	10	11
4	5	6	7	8	9	10
3	4	5	6	7	8	9
2	3	4	5	6	7	8
1	2	3	4	5	6	7
	1	2	3	4	5	6

Find:

1) ***P*(Score of 8)** = ...

2) ***P*(a double)** = ...

3) ***P*(an odd score)** = ...

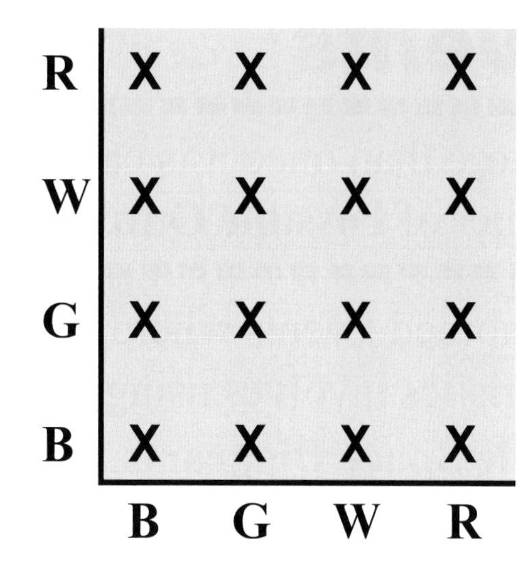

A bag contains four balls of different colours: Black, Grey, White and Red. A ball is drawn out at random and then put back. The bag is shaken and another ball is drawn out. The results are displayed on the Diagram.

There are **16 Possible Outcomes**.

Find: 4) ***P*(2 reds)** = ... 5) ***P*(red + white)** = ...

6) ***P*(2 balls of the same colour)** = ...

7) ***P*(2 balls of different colours)** = ...

Note - ***P*(balls of the same colour)** and ***P*(balls of different colours)** are **Mutually Exclusive Events**, since they do not have any common Outcomes.

A die and a coin are thrown. The Possible Outcomes are recorded on the Diagram.

H	X	X	X	X	X	X
T	X	X	X	X	X	X
	1	2	3	4	5	6

8a) ***P*(heads)** = ... b) ***P*(tails + 2)** = ...

c) ***P*(tails + even number)** = ...

Information from Surveys does not usually have Symmetry Characteristics so Theoretical Techniques do not apply. Probabilities can be worked out using:

Sample Tree Diagrams **Two-Way Tables**

In Sample Tree Diagrams Probabilities are written on Branches and Multiplied to find the final Probabilities.

Example: Record the pattern of Jeevan's attendance at registration over a two day period. What is the Probability Jeevan will be late on:
a) one day only? b) both days?

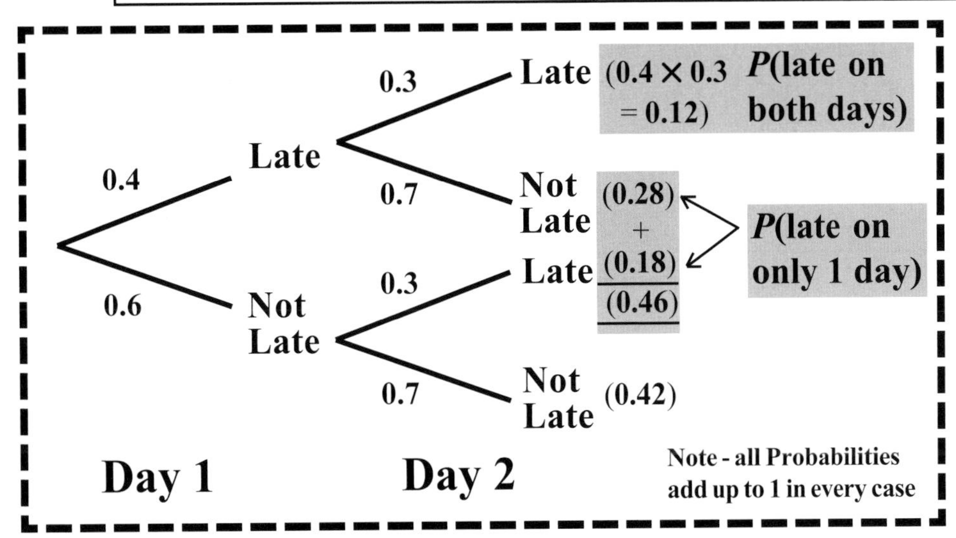

a) Late one day only - Add to combine the alternative end points. $\mathbf{0.28 + 0.18 = 0.46}$

b) Late both days - Multiply along the Branches.
$\mathbf{0.4 \times 0.3 = 0.12}$

Exercise 11: 5b Work out the Probabilities:

Score

9) A pile of books are sorted into hardbacks (**HB**) and paperbacks (**PB**). The first two choices recorded on a Sample Tree Diagram.

What is the Probability that:

a) Both books will be paperback?

***P*(paperback)** = ...

b) Only one will be a hardback?

***P*(hardback)** = ...

0.3 HB
0.3 HB
0.7 PB
0.7 PB
0.4 HB
0.6 PB
First Choice
Second Choice

Two-Way Tables show more than one Possible Outcome.

Example:

A Two-Way Table shows pupils in a class whose favourite sports are either football or swimming.

a) If a boy is chosen at Random, what is the Probability he likes football?

b) If a person is chosen at Random, what is the Probability he or she will like Swimming?

Sport	Boys	Girls	Total
Football	4	6	10
Swimming	7	17	24
Total	11	23	34

a) The Probability a Random boy will like football: $P(\text{a boy likes football}) = \frac{4}{11}$

b) The Probability a Random person will like swimming: $P(\text{swimming}) = \frac{24}{34} = \frac{12}{17}$

Exercise 11: 5c Answer the following:

10) A Two-Way Table shows the choices of milkshake made by a class.

Milkshake	Boys	Girls	Total
Vanilla	10	6	16
Banana	6	8	14
Total	16	14	30

What is the Probability:

a) a Random girl likes vanilla? ***P*(vanilla)** = ...

b) a Random child likes banana? ***P*(banana)** = ...

Chapter Twelve

LINES and ANGLES

1. Types of Line

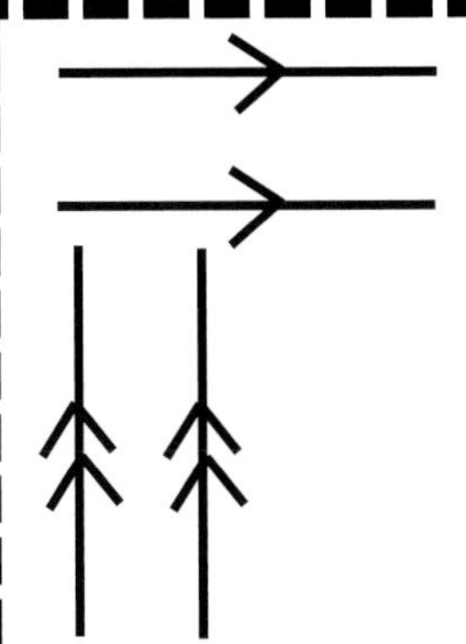

Two Lines drawn in the same direction, but never meeting are called **Parallel Lines** (indicated by arrows).

A Line drawn straight 'up' or 'down' or exactly upright is a **Vertical Line**.

A Line drawn straight'across' parallel to the horizon is a **Horizontal Line**.

When a Horizontal Line meets a Vertical Line the two Lines are **Perpendicular** to each other. $\perp$ means **'is Perpendicular to'**

Lines of **Equal Length** are indicated with little dashes.

A straight Line sloping from one corner of a Shape to another is a **Diagonal**.

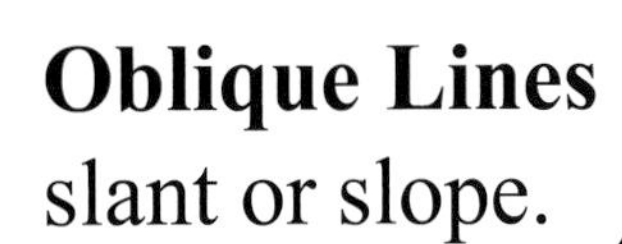

Oblique Lines slant or slope.

Collinear Points are points lying on a straight Line.

A Line which halves another Line is said to **Bisect** it (Line AB bisects Line CD).

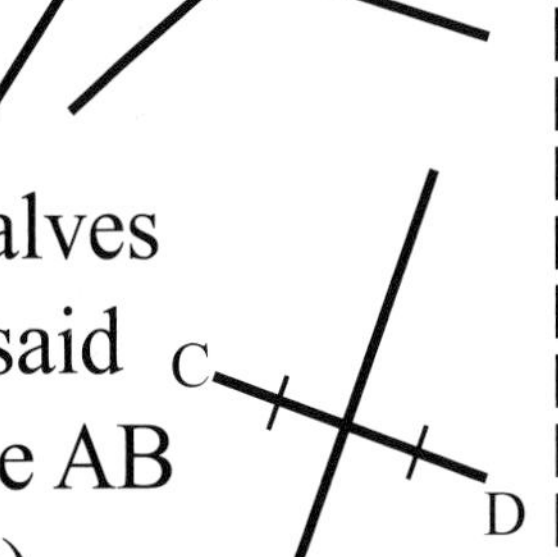

Exercise 12: 1a Answer the following:

1) The floor and ceiling of this room are .... (Vertical, Parallel, Perpendicular).

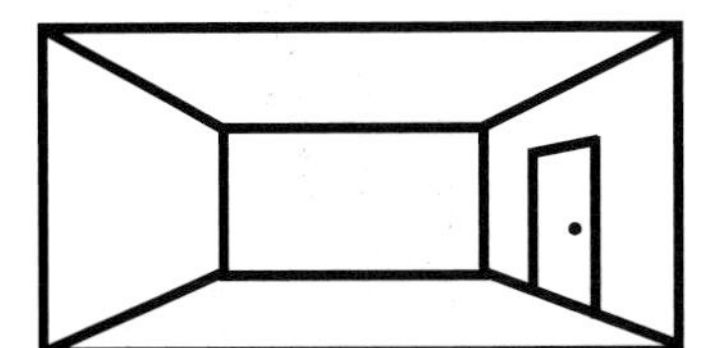

2) Each rung on a ladder is .... to the Sides of the ladder. (Parallel, Perpendicular, Horizontal).

3) How many Horizontal Sides does this shape have? It has .... Horizontal Sides.

4) Railway tracks are .... (Perpendicular, Vertical, Parallel).

5) How many Vertical Sides does this shape have? It has .... Vertical Sides.

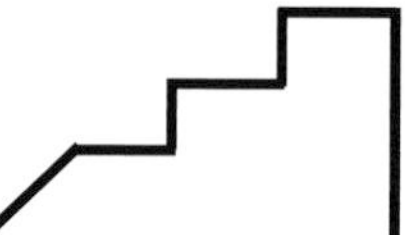

2. Types of Angle

Angles are formed when two Straight Lines meet. Angles are measured in Degrees. The symbol for Degrees is °
A **complete turn** is **360°**. Right-hand turns are **Clockwise** (as the Clock) and left-hand turns are **Anti-Clockwise**.

The diagram shows a Line as it turns through 4 Right Angles.

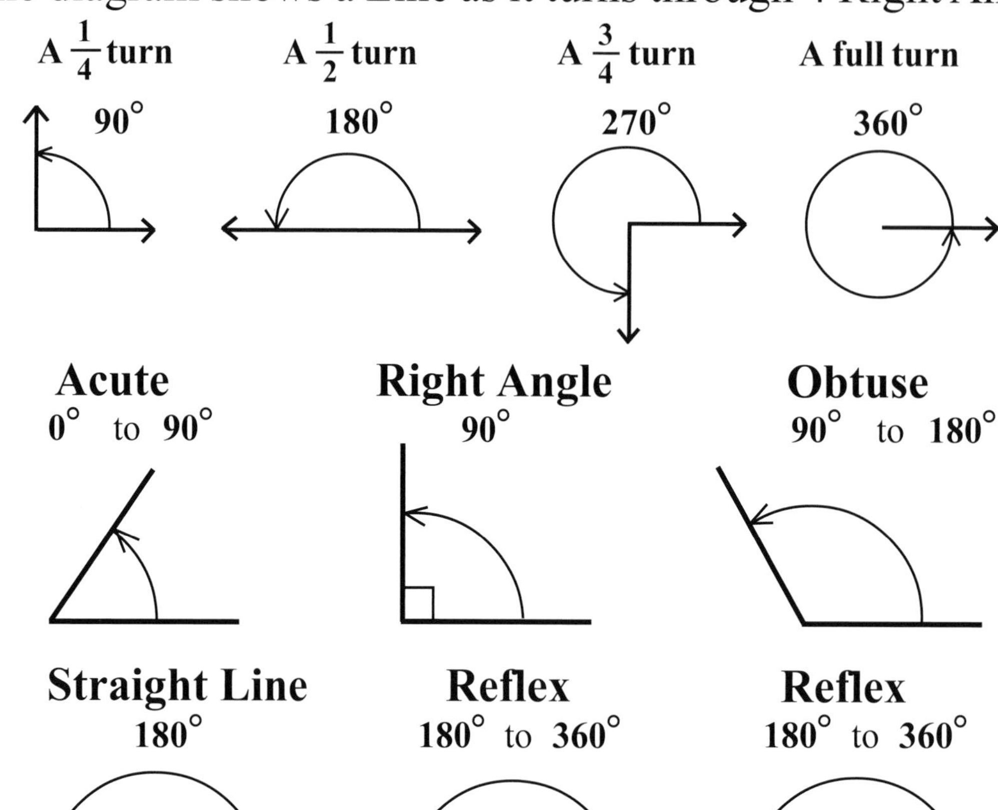

Exercise 12: 1b

Score

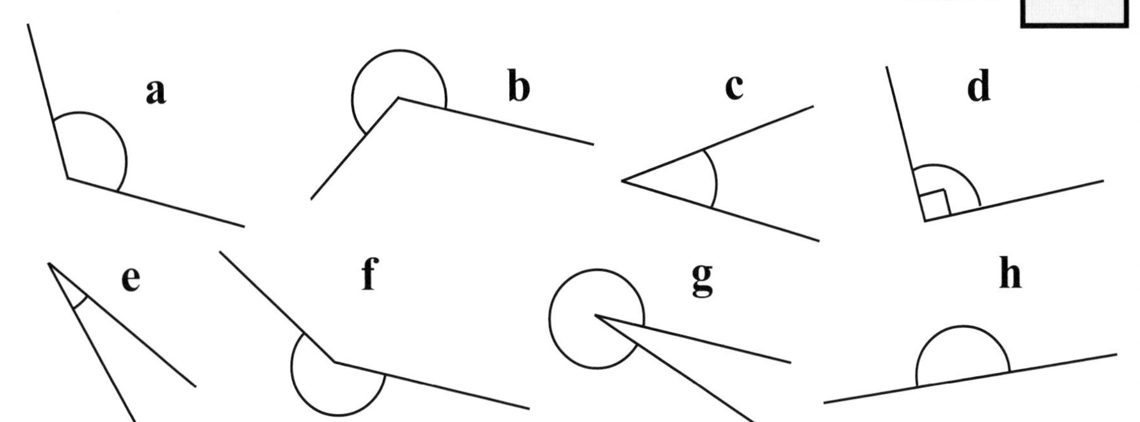

6) Which two Angles show a $\frac{1}{4}$ turn and a $\frac{1}{2}$ turn? ....
7) Which two Angles are acute? ....
8) Which three Angles are bigger than **180°**? ....
9) Is angle **a** Reflex, Obtuse or Acute? ....
10) What name is given to Angles **b**, **f**, and **g**? ....

3. Line and Angle Relationships

Angle Relationships between Parallel and Intersecting Lines.

Complementary

Two Angles Added together to make **90°**.

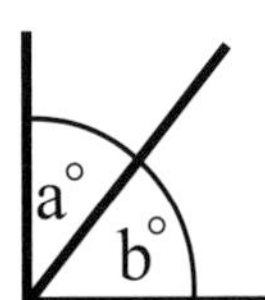

Supplementary

Two Angles Added together to make **180°**.

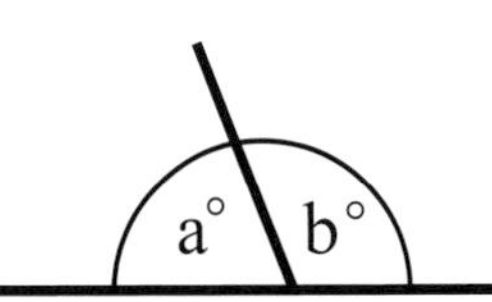

Conjugate

Two Angles Added together to make **360°**.

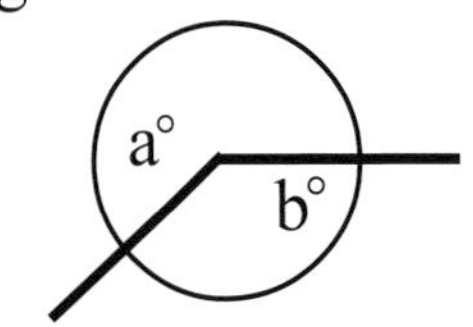

Opposite

a = d and b = c

a and d and b and c are Vertically Opposite.

Adjacent

a & b : b & d : d & c

c & a are Adjacent.

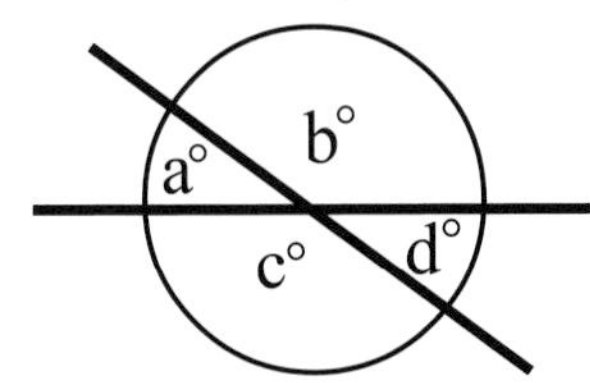

Alternate

a = c

a and c are Alternate.

Interior/Allied

a + b = 180°

a and b are Allied/Interior.

(A Line across 2 Parallel Lines is called a **Transversal**).

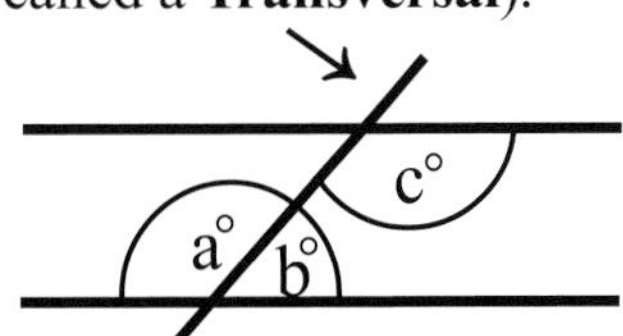

Corresponding

a = b

The two Equal Angles are Corresponding.

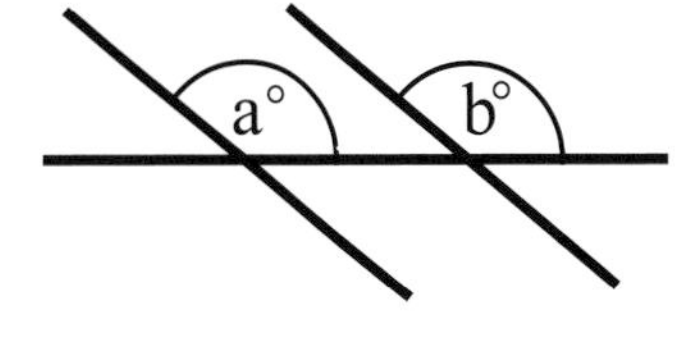

Missing Angles can be found by Subtraction.

Example:

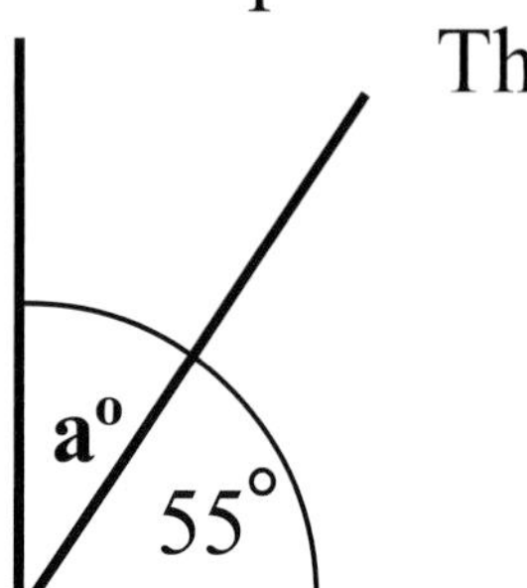

These **Complementary** Angles add up to 90°.

Angle a can be found by **Subtracting**.

$$90^\circ - 55^\circ = 35^\circ$$

Angle a = 35°.

Exercise 12: 2 Answer the following: **Score**

Write the **Missing Angle** and **Line/Angle Relationship**:

1)

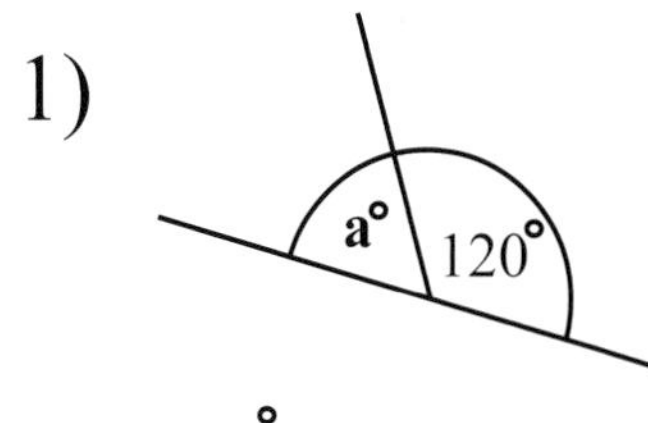

a = ...°

.... Angle

2)

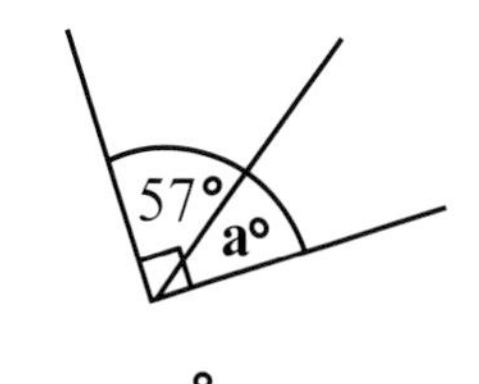

a = ...°

.... Angle

3)

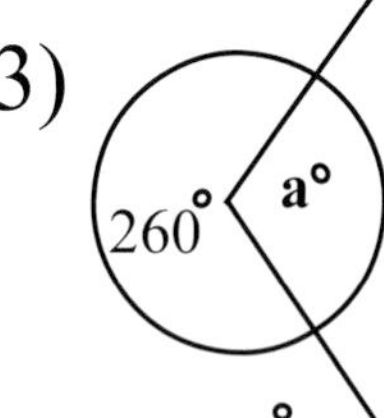

a = ...°

.... Angle

4)

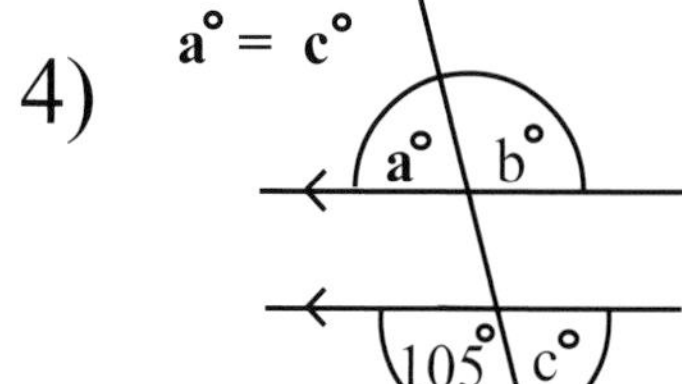

a = ...°

a and c are.................... Angles

5)

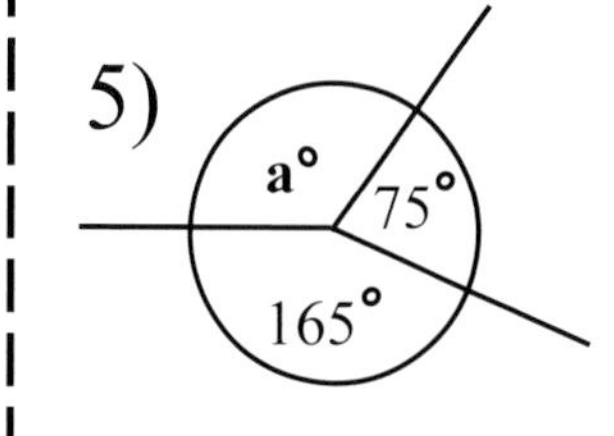

a = ...°

.... Angle

6)

a = ...°

.... Angle

7)

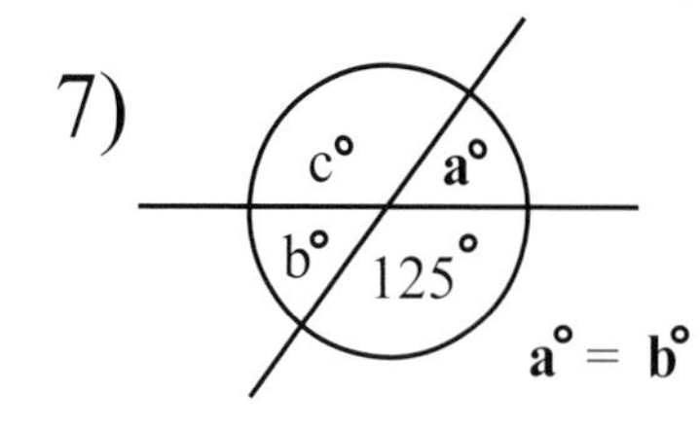

a = ...°

c and a .... Angles

8)

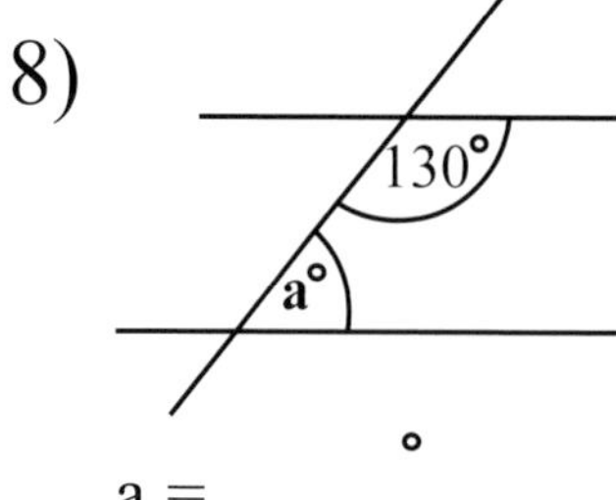

a = ...°

.... Angle

9)

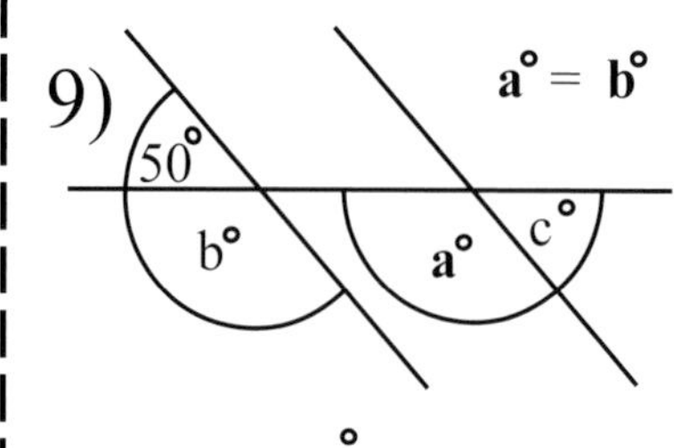

a = ...°

a and b .... Angles

10) Describe these Angles by using Acute, Obtuse, Reflex.

108° .... **43°** .... **279°** ....

4. Angles and Fractions

Fractions can be calculated if Degrees are given.

Example: What is Angle **a** as a Fraction of the Circle?

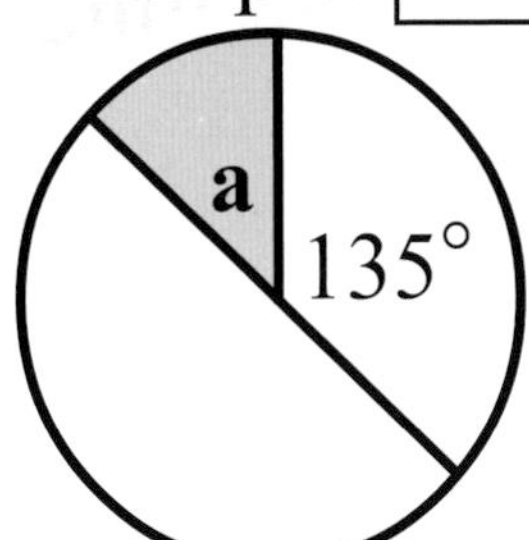

a is **Supplementary** $180^\circ - 135^\circ = 45^\circ$

Write as a Fraction and Simplify $\frac{45^{1}}{360_{8}}$

45° as a **Fraction** is $\frac{1}{8}$

Exercise 12: 3a Write the Missing Angle as a Fraction:

1) 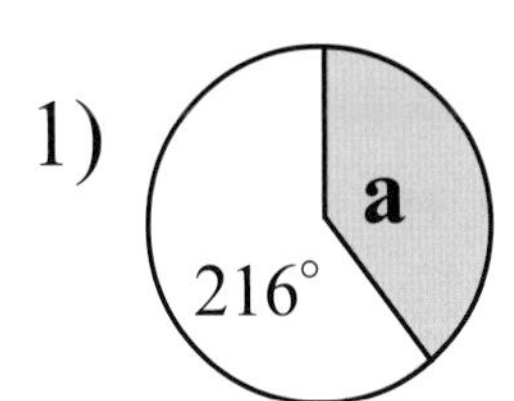

....

2) a, 108° ....

3) a, 120° ....

Express as a Fraction: 4) 210° = ... 5) 24° = ...

Degrees can be calculated if Fractions are given.

Example: What is Angle **a** in Degrees?

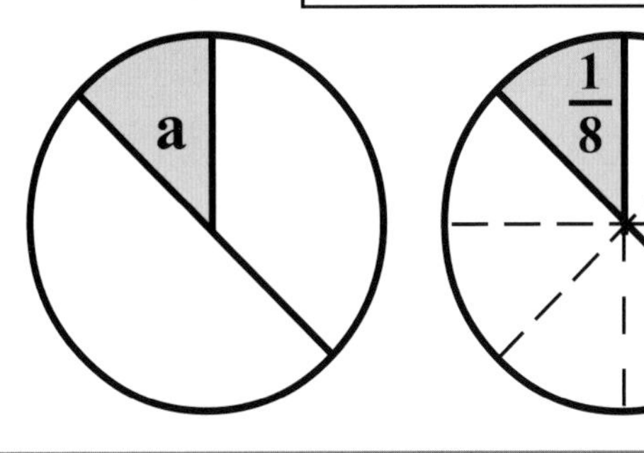

Drawing in the Missing Lines shows it is $\frac{1}{8}$

Multiply by 360 $\frac{1}{8} \times \frac{360}{1}$ (cancelling: $\frac{1}{\not{8}_{1}} \times \frac{\not{360}^{45}}{1}$)

$\frac{1}{8}$ in **Degrees** is 45°

Exercise 12: 3b Write the Angle in Degrees:

Score

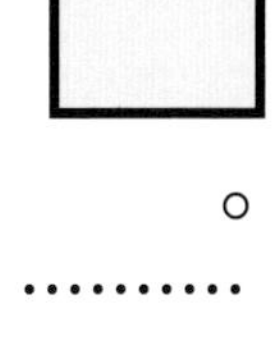

6) 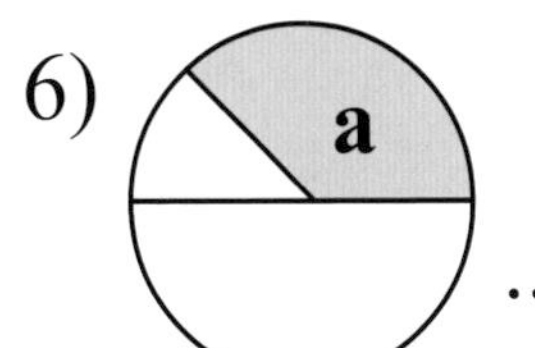

.........°

7) 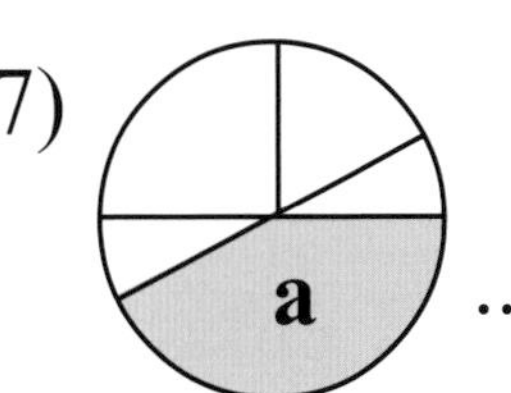

..........°

8) 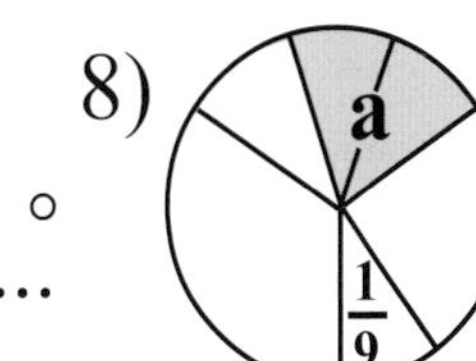

..........°

Express in Degrees: 9) $\frac{2}{3}$ = ...° 10) $\frac{5}{6}$ = ...°

5. Bearings and Directions

a. The Compass

The eight Compass Directions are termed **Bearings**.

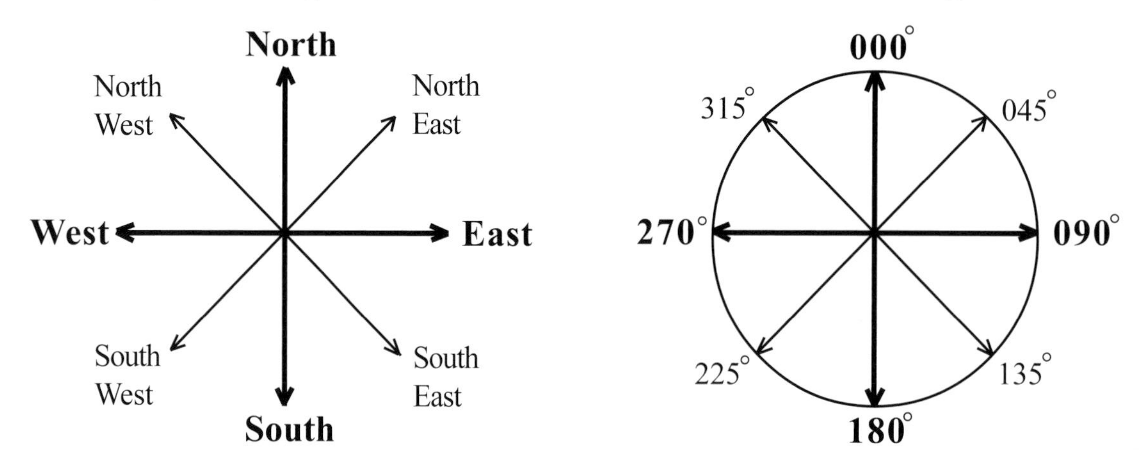

- It is important to know the **8 points** of the Compass and their Measurements in Degrees e.g. **270°** is west.
- All Bearings are written in Degrees as 3 figures. e.g. **060°**.
- All Bearings are measured Clockwise from the **Northline**.
- A **Full Turn** of the Compass will be **four Right Angles**.

b. Finding a Bearing

Bearings are expressed in degrees or directions and can be measured with a protractor (none is required here).

Examples:

North

A 090° B

Bearing 1 from A to B is 090° east.

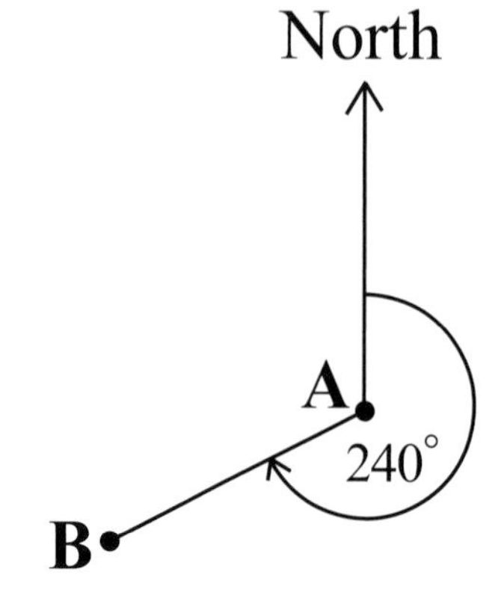

Bearing 2 from A to B is 240° and is approximately south-west.

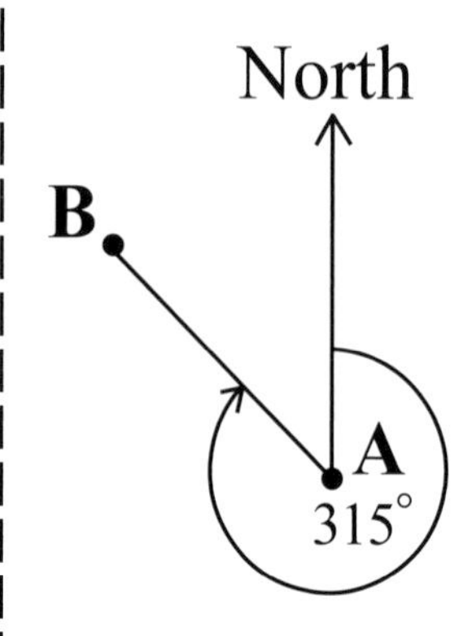

Bearing 3 from A to B is 315° north-west.

Exercise 12: 4 Calculate the following:

1) Using a Compass, a man walks on a Bearing of **135°**.
In what Direction is he travelling? ....

2) A ship sailed in a **north easterly** direction.
What is the Bearing from A to B? ....°

3) Paul is facing **west**. If he turned Clockwise through **3** Right Angles, in what Direction would he be facing?
He would be facing ....

4) Judy is facing **south**. If she turned Anti-clockwise through an Angle of **270°** in what Direction would she be facing? She would be facing ....

5) John walks on a Bearing of **225°**. He changes Direction and walks due **east**. What Degree difference is there between the Bearings? It is .... degrees.

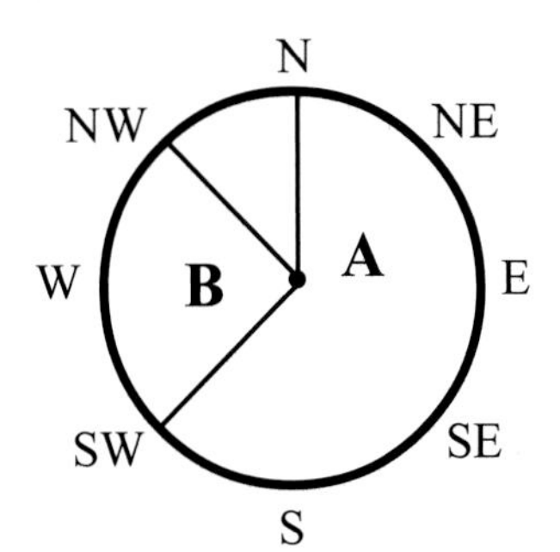

6) What is the size of Angle **A**?
Angle **A** is .... degrees.

7) What is the size of Angle **B**?
Angle **B** is .... degrees.

8) A boy is facing **east**. He spins round Anti-clockwise **180°**. Then he spins Clockwise for **270°**. In what Direction is he now facing? He is facing ....

9) Pat looks **east** and sees the sun rise. Later she watches the sun set in the **west**. How many Degrees difference is there between the two Directions? It is .... degrees.

10) If Simon faces **south-east** and turns **3** Right Angles Anti-clockwise, in what Direction is he now facing?
He is now facing ....

Score

c. Back Bearings

Back Bearings are calculated from the opposite direction to the given Bearing. To find a Back Bearing:

1. Draw in a new Northline where the measure is to be taken from.
2. Use the properties of Parallel Lines and Angles to find the Back Bearing.

Example:

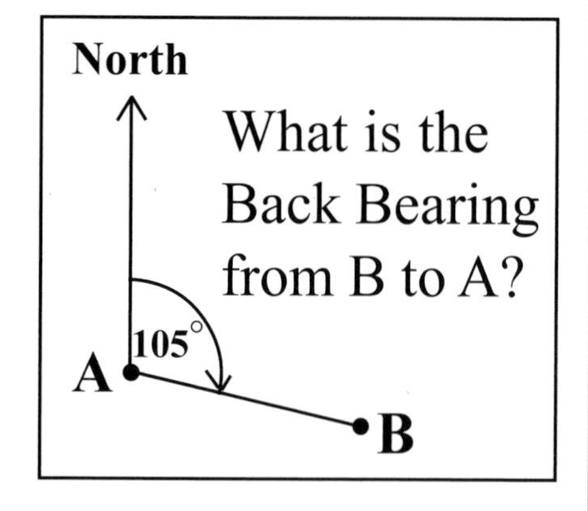

a. Draw in a new Northline at B as the Back Bearing is measured from B to A.

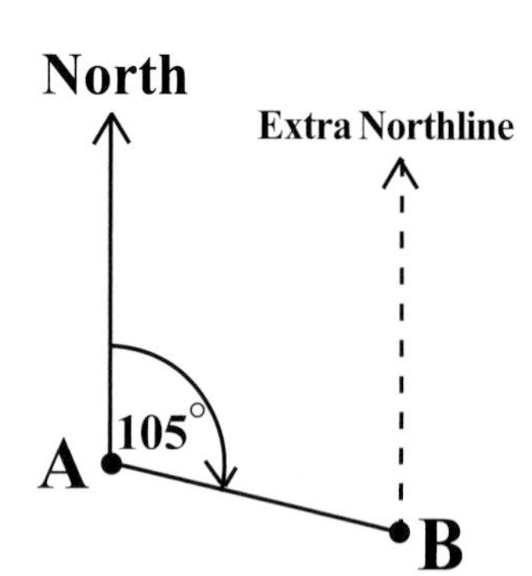

b. Extend the Northline at A to make a **180°** Angle. The Supplementary Angle must be **75°**.

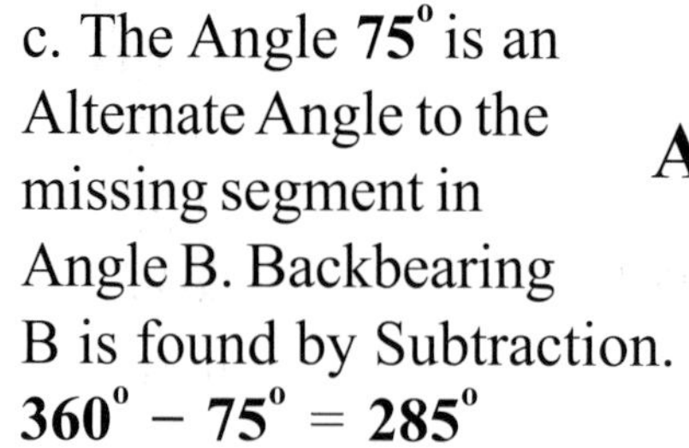

c. The Angle **75°** is an Alternate Angle to the missing segment in Angle B. Backbearing B is found by Subtraction.

360° − 75° = 285°

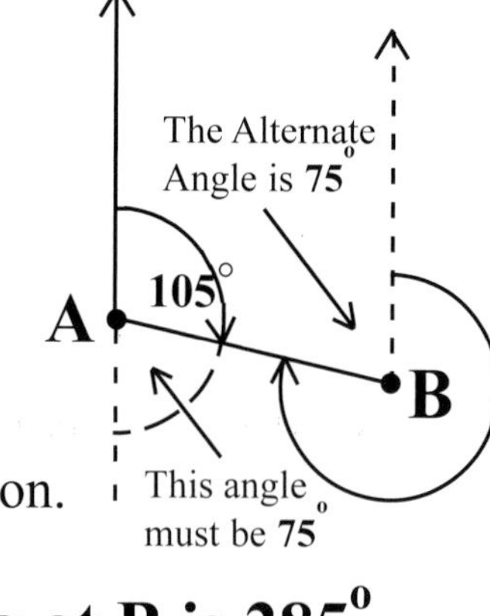

The Back Bearing at B is 285°

Exercise 12: 5 Calculate the following:

What are the Back Bearings of A from B in the following:

1) The Back Bearing is ....°

2) The Back Bearing is ....°

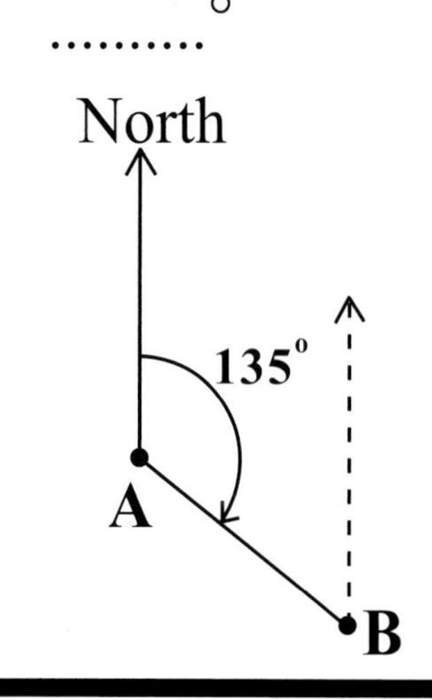

In the first two questions an extra Northline has been drawn in at point B to help with the calculation.

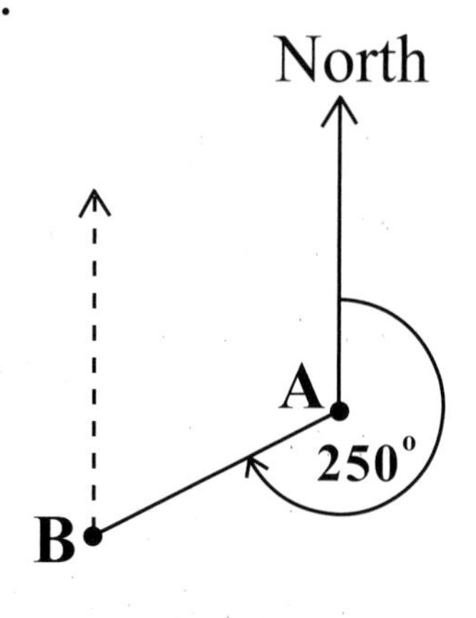

3) A ship sets sail but continually adjusts its course to avoid bad weather. So the ship can return easily to the previous position the Back Bearing is always calculated. Give each Back Bearing:

a) A from B ....°
b) B from C ....°
c) C from D ....°
d) D from E ....°

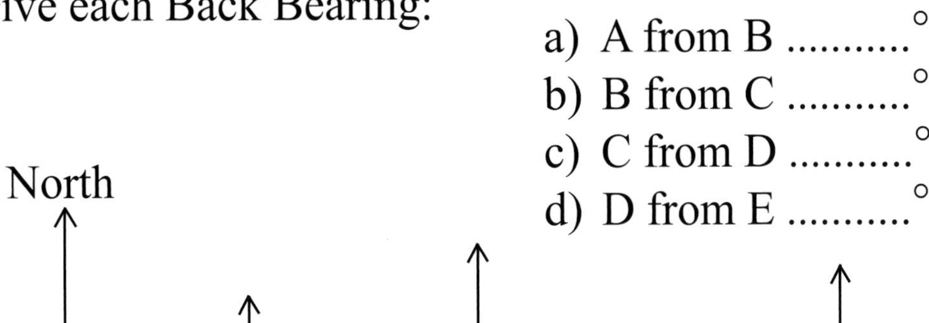

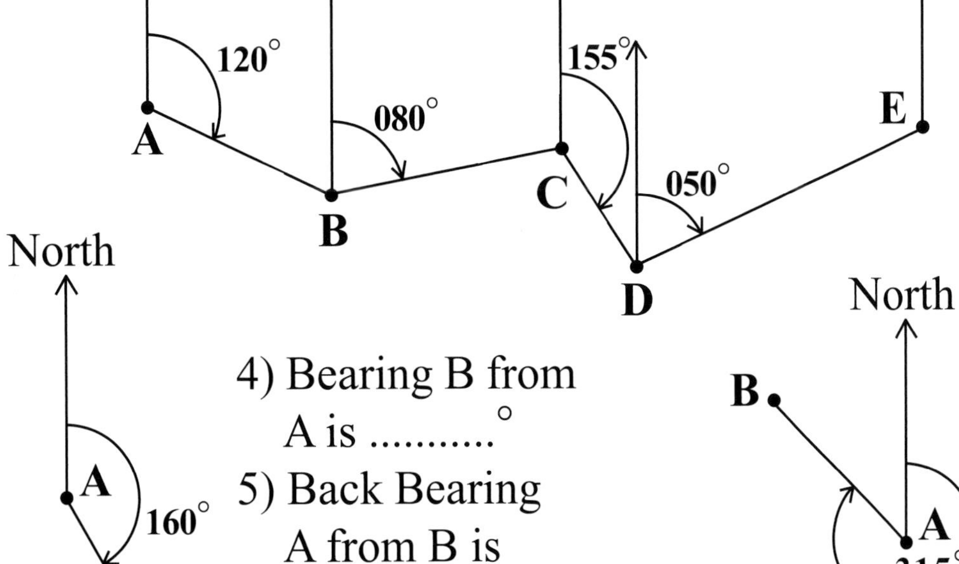

4) Bearing B from A is ....°

5) Back Bearing A from B is ....°

North
B
A
315°

6) Bearing B from A is ....°

7) Back Bearing A from B is ....°

8) Bearing B from A is ....°

9) Back Bearing A from B is ....°

North
A
B
270°

North
A
50°
B

10) Back Bearing A from B is ....°

Score

Chapter Thirteen

TIME

1. Time Measurement

a. The Calendar (Gregorian)

For the **Millennium**:

1000 Years = **1** Millennium

For the **Century**:

100 Years = **1** Century

For the **Decade**:

10 Years = **1** Decade

For the **Year**:

365 Days = **1** Year

366 Days = **1** Leap Year

(A Leap Year is every **4** Years - 1996, 2000, 2004)

12 Months = **1** Year

52 Weeks = **1** Year

For the **Months**:

30 Days have September, April, June and November. All the rest have **31**, except February alone which has **28** Days clear, but **29** in each Leap Year.

Note: **4** Months have **30** Days
7 Months have **31** Days
1 Month has **28/29** Days

1 Lunar Month = **4** weeks

13 Lunar Months = **1** year

For the **Week**:

7 Days in **1** Week (Sun 1st day)

14 Days in **1** Fortnight

Counting Centuries:

BC means 'Before the birth of Christ'; BCE means Before Common Era

AD means 'Anno Domini' (Latin for 'in the Year of the Lord'); CE means Common Era

← **BC or BCE** | **AD or CE** →

Years	499 - 400	399 - 300	299 - 200	199 - 100	99 - 0	0 - 99	100-199	200-299	300-399	400-499
Century	5th	4th	3rd	2nd	1st	1st	2nd	3rd	4th	5th

↑ The Year 250 BC (BCE) was in the Third Century BC (BCE)

↑ **Birth of Christ**

↑ The Year 250 AD (CE) was in the Third Century AD (CE)

Centuries are counted forward or backwards from the birth of Christ. 250 AD (CE) is in the third Century after Christ, but 250 BC (BCE) is in the third Century before Christ.

The Year **1999** was in the **Twentieth Century**

We are in the **21st Century** and the **3rd Millennium**

Years	1700-1799	1800-1899	1900-1999	2000-2099
Century	18th	19th	20th	21st

b. Other Time Measurements

The Seasons of the Year

The four seasons are **Spring**, **Summer**, **Autumn**, **Winter**.

The seasons are linked to the distance of the Earth from the Sun at different times of the year.

Vernal Equinox - first day of Spring is usually the 20th or 21st March. There are exactly 12 hours daylight and 12 hours darkness.

Summer Solstice - first day of Summer is usually the 20th or 21st June. This is the longest day of the year.

Autumn Equinox - first day of Autumn is usually the 22nd or 23rd September. There are exactly 12 hours daylight and 12 hours darkness.

Winter Solstice - first day of Winter is usually the 21st or 22nd December. This is the shortest day of the year.

British Summer Time

This is the Clock time used in 'Summer' (March to October). The Clocks go forward one hour in March and back one hour in October. This gives us more morning daylight time during Winter.

Greenwich Mean Time (GMT)

This is the standard Clock time which is used in Britain and some Western European countries. GMT is based on the Greenwich Meridian Line at the Royal Observatory in Greenwich (near The O2 Arena).

International Date Line

This is the line of Longitude which goes from North to South in the Pacific Ocean. It is used as a means of ending one day and starting the next. The earth is divided up into Time Zones based on the lines of Longitude. At 12 midday in Greenwich it will be 12 midnight at the International Date Line.

Exercise 13: 1a   Work out the following:

1) How many Decades are there in a **Century**? .... decades.
2) How many Years are there in **two Millennia**? .... years.
3) **1996** was a Leap Year. Will **2016** be a Leap Year? ....
4) The Year **2005** is in which Century? .... century.
5) How many Months are there between **1st March 1989** and **1st May 1992**? .... months.
6) How many Months in a Year have **31 days**? .... months.
7) A man was born in **1962**; he'll be **60** Years old in ....

Calculating the **Number of Days**.

Example: **How many Days are there from the 21st January 1999 to 8th March 1999?**

(Do not include the 8th)

Jan 21st → End Jan → End Feb → 8th March

11 Days   28 Days   7 Days

Add them to get the total number of Days

11 + 28 + 7 = **46 Days**

If it says **from**, then include the **first** Day.

When counting Days do not count Dates.

From 1st - 8th March : Total of 7 (Days) not 8 (Dates)

1st →(1) 2nd →(2) 3rd →(3) 4th →(4) 5th →(5) 6th →(6) 7th →(7 days) 8th March

Exercise 13: 1b   Work out the following:

8) How many Days are there between **01. 12. 82** and **14. 02. 83**? (Exclude 01. 12. 82 and 14. 02. 83) .... days.
9) How many Days altogether in **May**, **June** and **July**? ....
10) How many Days are there from **26th May** to **4th June**? (Exclude 4th June) .... days.

Score 

2. Dates

Writing **Dates In Numbers** and **In Full**. Always use two digits for the Day and Month.

Example: **In Numbers** **08. 12. 99** **In Full** **8th December 1999**

Exercise 13: 2 Answer the following:

Write the following Dates **In Numbers**:

1) **14th April 1975** _______ 2) **20th August 1955** ______

3) **1st February 1920** _______ 4) **11th May 1963** ______

5) **22nd December 1997** _______

Write the following Dates **In Full**:

6) **10. 11. 54** .... 7) **03. 07. 89** ....

8) **17. 03. 74** .... 9) **14. 09. 96** ....

10) **22. 10. 45** ....

Score

Calculating Dates using the Calendar.

Example:

What **Day** is the **28th May?**

April						
Su	M	Tu	W	Th	F	Sa
		1	2	3	4	5
6	7	8	9	10	11	12

1. Go to the last Day given
   12th April is a Saturday
   Keep Adding 7 till the end of the Month.
   12th - Add 7
   19th - Add 7
   26th - This is a Saturday

2. Deal with the cross-over to the next Month.

Sa	Su	M	Tu	W	Th	F
26	27	28	29	30	1	

1st May is a Thursday

3. Keep Adding 7 to get to the Date.

1st - Add 7
8th - Add 7
15th - Add 7
22nd - This is a Thursday

4. Work through to the Date.

Th	F	Sa	Su	M	Tu	**W**
22	23	24	25	26	27	**28**

The 28th May is a Wednesday.

Exercise 13: 3

Work out the following:

Write the **Date in Figures <u>2 Weeks</u> after the following**:

1) **26th February 1999** .... 2) **24. 12. 81** ....

3) **27. 06. 97** .... 4) **10th November 1974** ....

Write the **Date in Figures <u>4 Weeks</u> after the following**:

5) **23. 02. 86** .... 6) **27th September 2000** ....

7) **13th August 1958** .... 8) **23. 04. 67** ....

---

9) If the last Date given is the **14th October**, on what **<u>Day</u>** will the **14th December** be?

....

October						
Su	M	Tu	W	Th	F	Sa
1	2	3	4	5	6	7
8	9	10	11	12	13	**14**

January						
Su	M	Tu	W	Th	F	Sa
			1	2	3	4
5	6	7	8	9	10	11

10) On what **<u>Day</u>** is the **24th of February**?

....

Score

3. The Clock

a. Measuring Time

Time is measured as follows:

1 Minute (Mins)	=	60 Seconds (Secs)
1 Hour (Hrs)	=	60 Minutes
1 Day	=	24 Hours

Seconds
3,600 Seconds in one Hour.
86,400 Seconds in one Day.
Minutes
1,440 Minutes in one Day.

Exercise 13: 4 Calculate the following:

Score

How many Minutes are there in:

1) **$1\frac{1}{2}$ hours** .... mins. 2) **4 hours** .... mins.

3) **$3\frac{1}{4}$ hours** .... mins.

Convert to Hours and Minutes:

4) **77mins** ..... hr ..... mins. 5) **91mins** ..... hr ..... mins.

6) **212mins** ..... hrs .... mins.

How many Seconds are there in:

7) **$2\frac{1}{2}$ minutes** .... seconds. 8) **5 minutes** .... seconds.

How many Minutes and Seconds are there in:

9) **89secs** ..... min ..... secs. 10) **200secs** ..... mins ..... secs.

b. Time and Fractions

A clock face can be Divided into Fractions.
Minutes to Fractions of an Hour (divide by 60).

Example: **20 Minutes** as a Fraction.

Divide by 20

Cancel $\frac{\not{20}^{\,1}}{\not{60}_{\,3}}$ **20 Minutes** = $\frac{1}{3}$ **Hour**

Fractions of an Hour to Minutes (multiply by 60).

Example: What is $\frac{1}{3}$ of an Hour?

Fraction → Minutes

$\frac{1}{\cancel{3}_1} \times \frac{\cancel{60}^{20}}{1}$ $\frac{1}{3}$ **Hour = 20 Minutes**

Exercise 13: 5 Calculate the following:

Score 

Convert Minutes to Fractions of an Hour:

1) **12mins** ...... hr. 2) **10mins** ...... hr. 3) **36mins** ...... hr.

4) **25mins** ...... hr. 5) **4mins** ...... hr.

Convert Fractions of an Hour to Minutes:

6) $\frac{5}{6}$**hr** .... mins. 7) $\frac{7}{10}$**hr** .... mins. 8) $\frac{4}{5}$**hr** .... mins.

9) $\frac{11}{12}$**hr** .... mins. 10) $\frac{3}{10}$**hr** .... mins.

c. Time and Degrees

The clock can be Divided into Degrees:

Each Minute is Equivalent to 6° $\frac{360^\circ}{60 \text{ mins}} = 6^\circ$

Example:

35 Minutes in Degrees would be:

$35 \times 6 = \mathbf{210^\circ}$

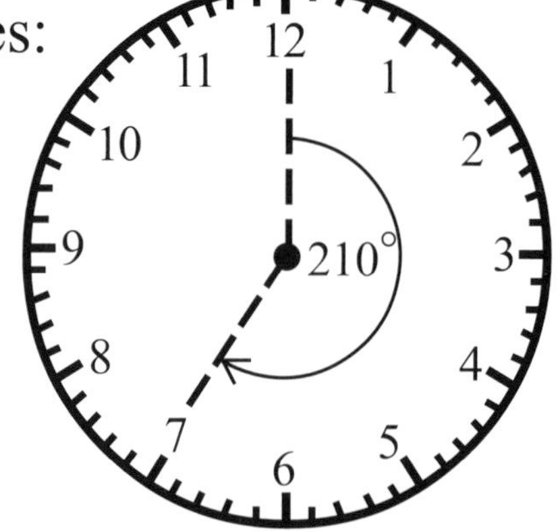

Minutes to Degrees.

Example:

What is **50 Minutes** in Degrees?

Multiply 50 by 6 $\mathbf{50 \times 6 = 300}$

50 Minutes is 300 Degrees.

Degrees to Minutes.
Example:

What is **300 Degrees** in Minutes?

Divide 300 by 6 $\frac{\mathbf{300}}{\mathbf{6}} = \mathbf{50}$

300 Degrees is 50 Minutes.

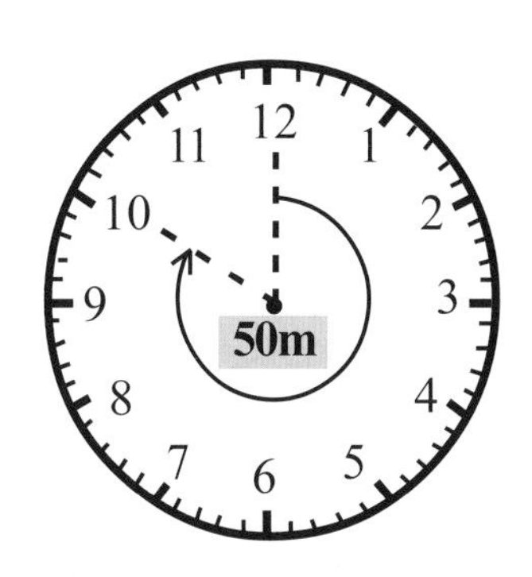

Exercise 13: 6 Calculate the following:

Score

Convert Minutes to Degrees:

1) **3mins** ....° 2) **10mins** ....° 3) **56mins** ....°

4) **12mins** ....° 5) **24mins** ....°

Convert Degrees to Minutes:

6) **36°** .... mins. 7) **330°** .... mins. 8) **246°** .... mins.

9) **102°** .... mins. 10) **234°** .... mins.

4. 12 and 24 Hour Time

12 Hour Clock (Analogue)

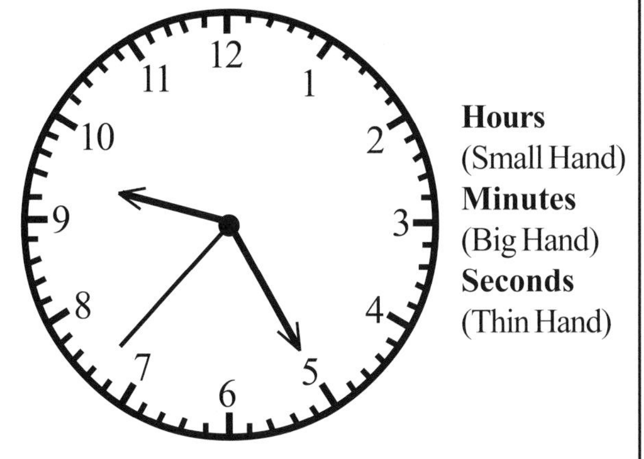

Hours (Small Hand)
Minutes (Big Hand)
Seconds (Thin Hand)

- Counts from Midnight to Noon, then Noon to Midnight.

a.m. - Ante Meridian (Before Noon)
Counts Midnight to Noon (Midday).

p.m. - Post Meridian (After Noon)
Counts Noon to Midnight.

24 Hour Clock (Digital)

Hours **Minutes** **Seconds**

09:25:37

- Counts from Midnight to Midnight.
- Hours are counted from 1 to 24.
- It is used for bus, rail and airline timetables.
- Time differences between countries are shown in 24 Hour Clock.

a. The 12 Hour System

Time **Written In Full** and **In Figures**.

12 o'clock midnight.
12.00 a.m.

Half past 12 a.m.
12.30 a.m.

- Times **In Full** are written above and Times **In Figures** are written beneath.
- The Times shown are after Midnight and **a.m.**
- On the Hour, **In Full** Times are followed by **o'clock**.

Up to the Half hour, <u>all</u> In Full Times are written **'past'**.

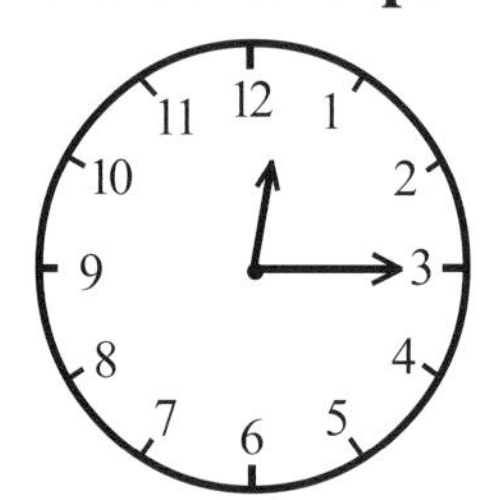

Quarter past 12 a.m.
12.15 a.m.

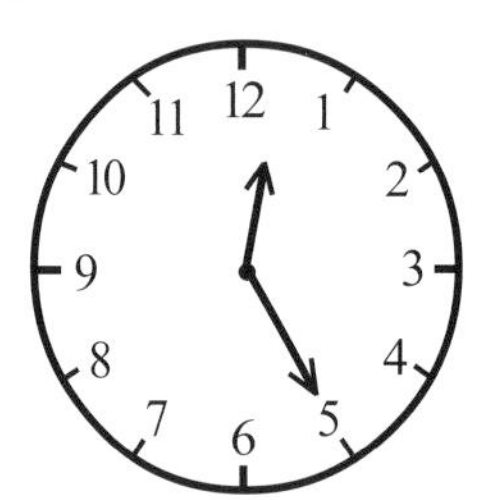

25 minutes past 12 a.m.
12.25 a.m.

After the Half hour, <u>all</u> In Full Times are written **'to'**.

Quarter to 1 a.m.
12.45 a.m.

5 minutes to 1 a.m.
12.55 a.m.

Exercise 13: 7 Write the Times <u>In Full</u> and <u>In Figures</u>:

1) 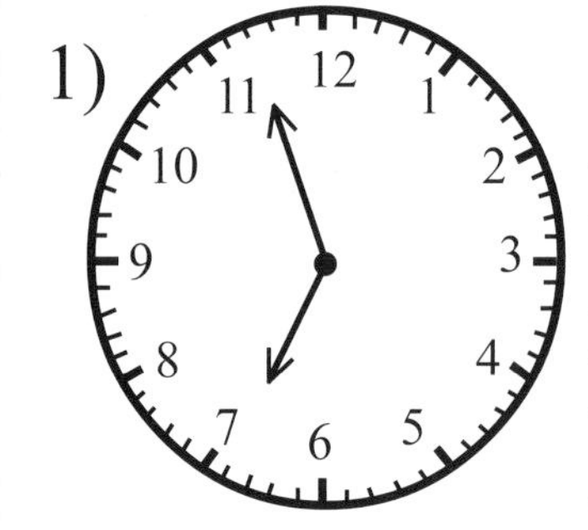

a.m.

In Full.

....

In Figures.

....

2) 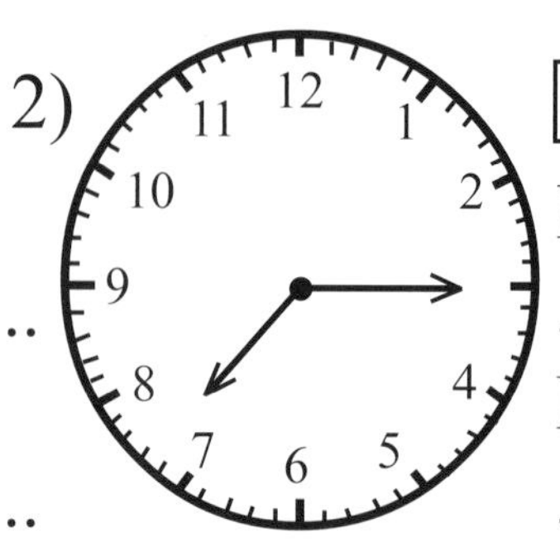

p.m.

In Full.

....

In Figures.

....

3) 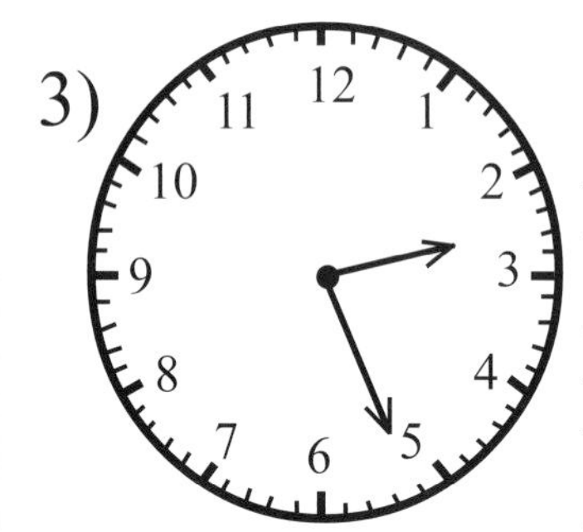

p.m.

In Full.

....

In Figures.

....

4) 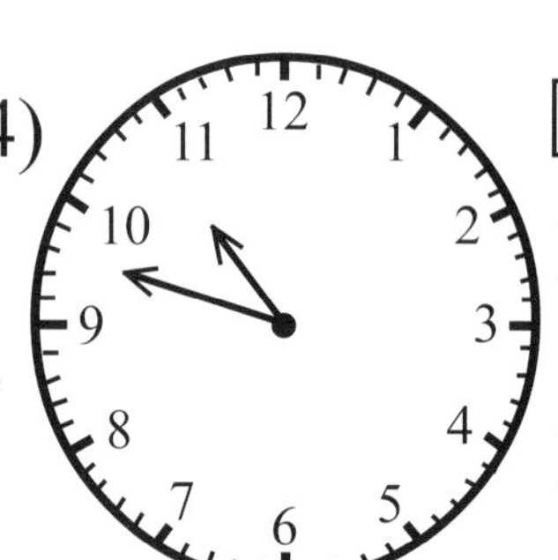

a.m.

In Full.

....

In Figures.

....

What would the **Real Time** be if the Analogue Clock was:

p.m.

5) **14 minutes fast**
(subtract 14mins).

In Full ....

In Figures ....

a.m.

6) **21 minutes slow**
(Add 21mins).

In Full ....

In Figures ....

a.m.

7) **29 minutes slow**
(Add 29mins).

In Full ....

In Figures ....

p.m.

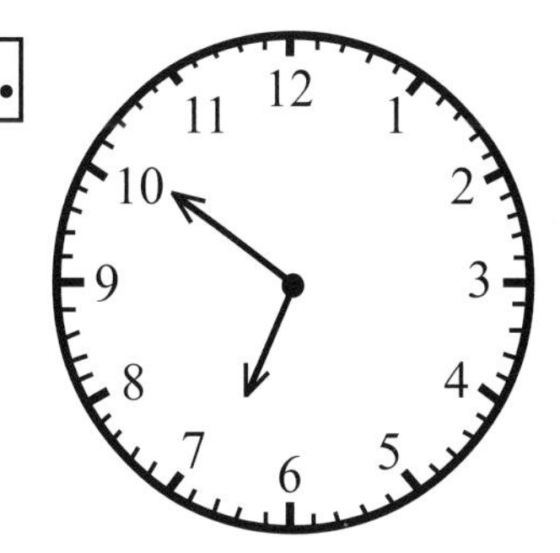

8) **44 minutes fast**
(Subtract 44mins).

In Full ....

In Figures ....

9) How many minutes must be **Added on** to take this Time forward to the next Hour?

.... minutes.

10) How many minutes must be **Subtracted** to take this Time back to the previous Hour?

.... minutes.

Score

b. The 24 Hour System

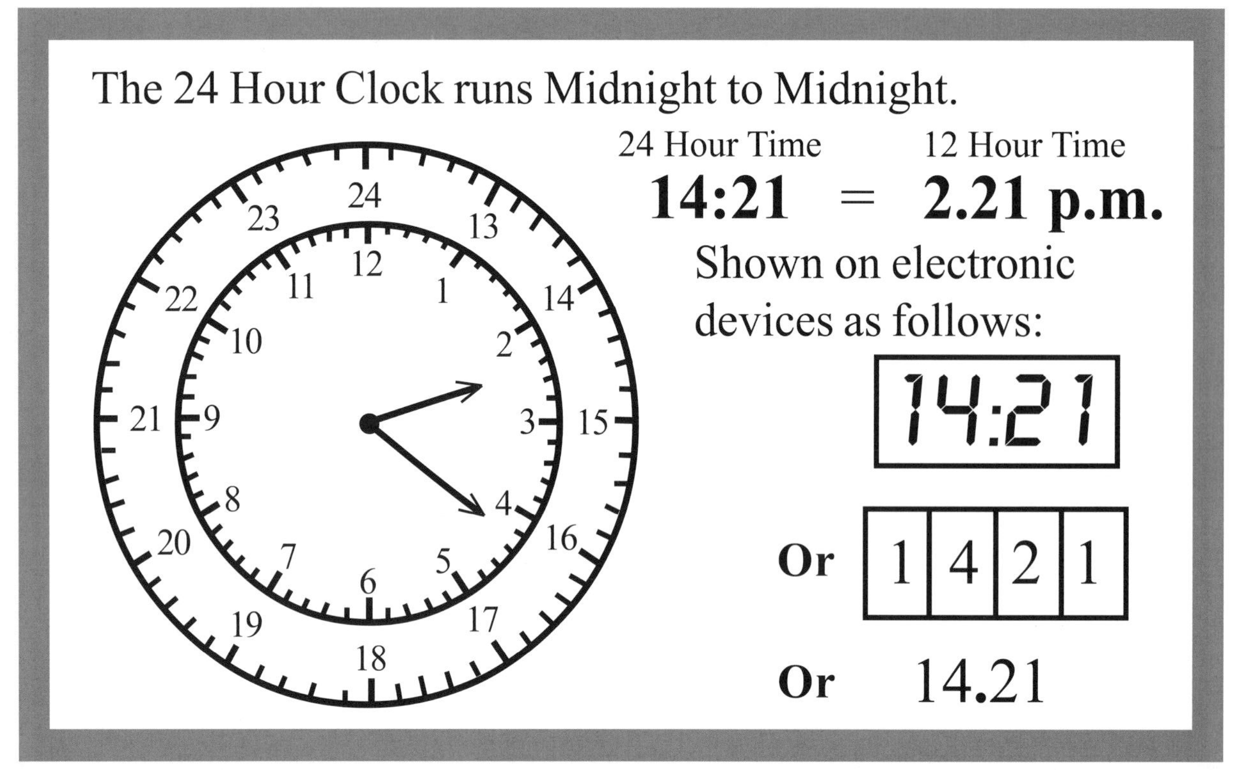

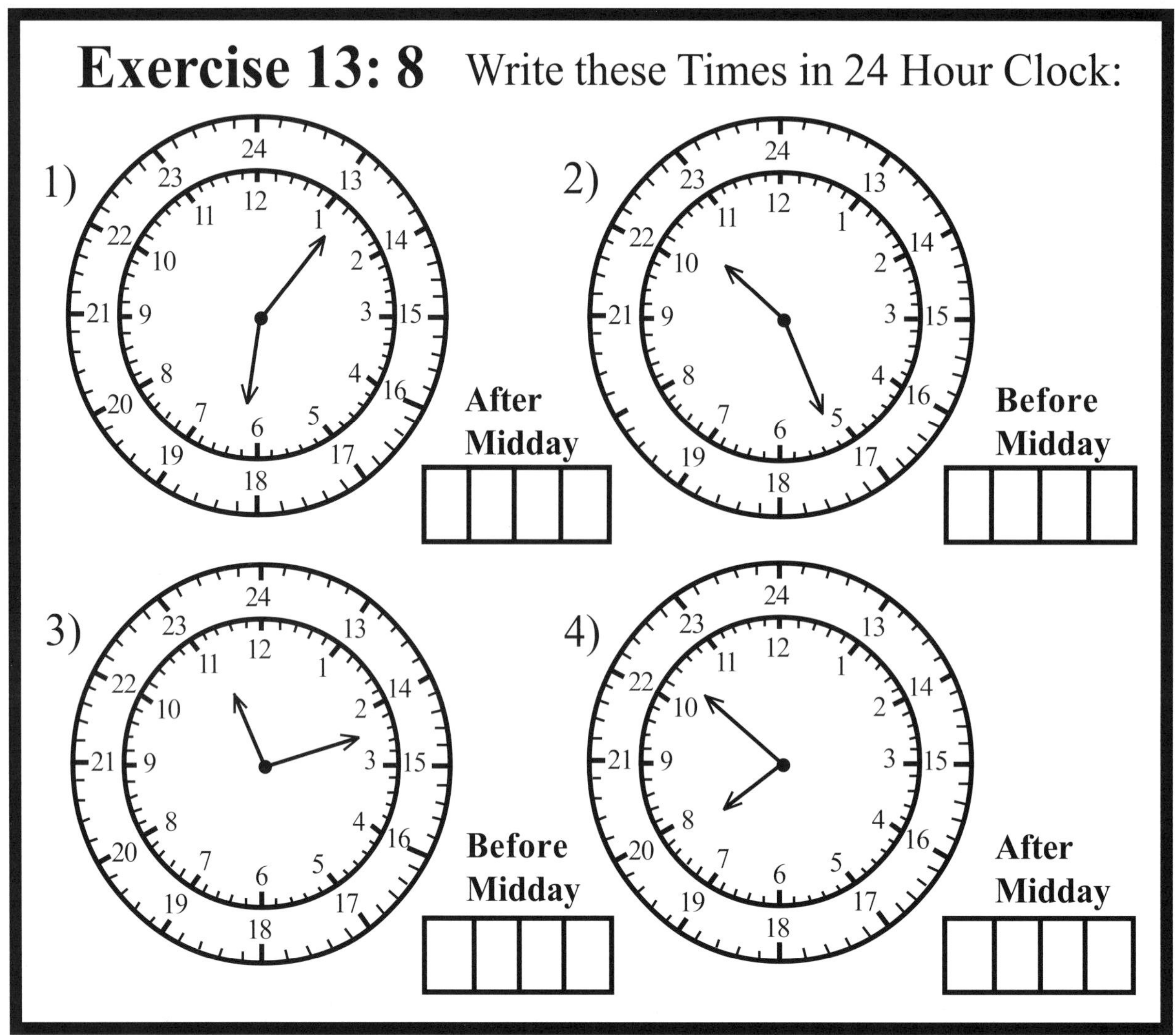

What would the **Real Time** be if the **Digital Clock** was:

5) **12 minutes slow** (Add 12mins).

1	5	3	2

6) **17 minutes fast** (Subtract 17mins).

2	3	4	3

7) **37 minutes fast** (Subtract 37mins).

0	3	5	0

8) **27 minutes slow** (Add 27mins).

1	8	2	1

---

9) If 4 trains leave at **13 minute** intervals, complete the following grids:

1	1	0	5

10) A different bus leaves every ten minutes. The journey takes **9 minutes**. Complete the table:

Depart	06:04	06:14	06:24	06:34	06:44
Arrive					

Score

c. 12 Hour and 24 Hour Conversions

12 Hour Clock (Analogue)	**24 Hour Clock (Digital)**
12 midnight.	00:00
4.30 a.m.	04:30
12.00 noon (midday).	12:00
2.15 p.m.	14:15
11.59 p.m.	23:59
(Two 12 hour periods).	(One 24 hour period).

Exercise 13: 9

Convert the following 12 Hour Times to 24 Hour Clock:

1) **Quarter to Nine a.m.**

2) **10.30 p.m.**

3) **12 midnight.**

4) **9.36 a.m.**

Convert the following 24 Hour Times to 12 Hour Clock:

5)

2	3	5	7

In Full.

....

In Figures.

....

6)

0	3	3	3

In Full.

....

In Figures.

....

7)

1	7	1	9

In Full.

....

In Figures.

....

8)

1	2	0	0

In Full.

....

In Figures.

....

9)

0	9	1	5

In Full.

....

In Figures.

....

10)

0	8	4	6

In Full.

....

In Figures.

....

5. Time Problems

a. Adding Time

Adding bigger Amounts of Time requires a method.
We use **Base 60** for the calculations (see **Book 2** for Bases).

Example:

A boy starts watching a video at **5.52 p.m.** It lasts for **2 Hours 27 Minutes**. At what Time does it finish?

Hours	Minutes	
17	**52**	
2	**27**	+
20	**19**	
1		

1. **Convert** to 24 Hour Clock.
2. **Calculation.**
   52 + 27 = 79mins
   Carry 1 into the Hours column
   Write **19** in the Mins column
   Add up Hours 17 + 2 + 1 = **20**
3. **Convert** back to 12 Hour Clock.
   20:19 = **8.19 p.m.**

The video finishes at **8.19 p.m.**

Exercise 13: 10a Calculate the following:

1) A man gets on a train at **1.14 p.m.** He journeys for **7 hours** and **53 minutes**. He changes to another train and journeys for a further **48 minutes**. When does he arrive?

Hours	Minutes	
13	**14**	
7	**53**	
	48	+

1. **Convert** to 24 Hour Clock.
2. **Calculate**.
3. **Convert** to 12 Hour Clock.

The man arrives at

.... p.m.

2) An aeroplane flies from Heathrow Airport at **00:35** and lands in Edinburgh **1 hour 27 minutes** later. What Time does it arrive?

Hours	Minutes	
0 0	**3 5**	
1	**2 7**	+

It arrives at .... hours.

3) Four children in the same class leave their school to go home. Fill in their arrival Times.

Children	**Claire**	**Peter**	**Anika**	**Nisha**
Leave School	3.30 p.m.	3.45 p.m.	3.35 p.m.	3.40 p.m.
Time Taken	37mins	63 mins	49mins	23mins
Arrive Home	**4.07 p.m.**	....	....	....

4) A girl stays to help at school for **25 minutes** on Monday, **34 minutes** on Tuesday and **15 minutes** on Wednesday. How much extra Time did she spend at school?

She spent .... hour .... minutes extra Time.

5) A man does overtime at work for a whole week. To receive his extra pay the Time must be added up.

His overtime adds up to:

.... hours .... mins.

Day	**Overtime**
Monday	**2hrs 45mins**
Tuesday	**1hr 10mins**
Wednesday	**1hr 50mins**
Thursday	**3hrs 35mins**
Friday	**1hr 50mins**

b. Subtracting Time

A period of Time can be found by Subtraction.
We use **Base 60** for the calculations (see **Book 2** for Bases).

Example:

A train leaves London at **15:46** and arrives at **Midnight** in Edinburgh. How long is the journey?

Hours	Minutes
~~24~~ 23	+60 0 0
1 5	4 6 –
8	1 4

1. **Write Midnight (00:00) as 24:00** in order to Subtract.
2. **Calculate**.
   00mins take away 46, cannot do
   Borrow 60mins; make 24 into 23
   $60 - 46 = \mathbf{14}$ $\quad 23 - 15 = \mathbf{8}$

The journey takes **8 hours 14 minutes**.

Exercise 13: 10b Calculate the following:

6) A boy helps at his school fête on a Saturday. He is there from **8.45 a.m.** to **6.25 p.m**. How long is he at the fête?

Hours	Minutes
~~18~~ 17	2 5 + 60
8	4 5 –

1. **Convert** to 24 Hour Clock.
2. **Calculate**.

The boy is at the fête for .... hours .... mins.

7) How many hours and minutes are there between **5.30 a.m.** and **19:57**?

1. **Convert** to 24 Hour Clock.
2. **Calculate** (no Borrowing is required on this sum).

There are .... hours .... mins.

Hours	Minutes
1 9	5 7
0 5	3 0 –

8) Four trains make journeys from London to Birmingham.

Trains	A	B	C	D
Paddington	09:31	10:16	12:20	14:12
Birmingham	13:21	15:10	15:53	17:01
Time Taken	**3hrs 50mins**	....	....	....

The **fastest** train is .... It took .... hours .... mins.

9) Work out the length of Time from **7.36 a.m.** to **10.17 p.m.** It is .... hours .... mins.

10) A girl watches television on a Saturday from **09:36** to **11:22**. She spends .... hour .... mins. watching television.

Score

c. Multiplying Time

The period of Time can be found by Multiplication.

This example uses **Base 60** and **Base 24** (see **Book 2** for Bases).

Example:

A secretary does **2 Hours 20 Minutes** extra work for a whole Month (**20 Working Days**). How much extra Time has she worked in total?

Days	Hours	Minutes
	2	20
		20 ×
1	22	40
1	6	

Calculate.

20 × 20 = 400: Write **40mins**

Carry 6 hrs (360 mins = 6 hrs)

20 × 2 = 40   40 + 6 = 46 hours

Carry 1 Day (24 hours), write **22 Hours**

Write **1 Day**

She works **1 Day, 22 Hours & 40 Minutes**.

Exercise 13: 11a Calculate the following:

1) A boy practises the piano for **1 hour 25 minutes** per day for a week. How long does he practise in total?

Hours	Minutes
1	25
	7 ×

The boy practises for .... hours .... mins.

2) A nurse works **8 nights**. Each shift is **13 hours 30 minutes** long. How long does she work in total?

Days	Hours	Minutes
	13	30
		8 ×

She works for ...... days ...... hours ...... mins.

3) A boy plays his computer game every day for **4 weeks**. Each time he plays the game it takes **3 minutes 30 seconds** to load. How much Time does he waste waiting for his game to load?

Hours	Minutes	Seconds
	3	30
		28 ×

He wastes .... hour ....mins .... secs.

4) A long film runs over **3 nights**. It is shown on television in segments of **1 hour 45 minutes**. How long is the whole film?

The film lasts .... hours .... mins.

5) A year 5 class have **35 minutes** reading Time each day for **2 school weeks**. How long do they spend in total?

They spend .... hours .... mins.

d. Dividing Time

The period of Time can be found by Division.
We use **Base 60** for this calculation (see **Book 2** for Bases).
Example:

A teacher Divides her Time equally between **5** children who need help. She has **3 Hours 20 Minutes** available. How much Time does she spend with each child?

	Hours	Minutes
	0	**40**
5	**3** (+ 180)	**20**

Calculate.
3 ÷ 5 won't go, Write **0 hrs**
Carry 3 hrs (180mins)
20 + 180 = 200mins
200 ÷ 5 = **40mins**

She spends **40 Minutes** with each child.

Exercise 13: 11b Calculate the following:

6) Sean shares Time on his computer equally with his two sisters. In an evening there are **5 hours 45 minutes** available. How long will Sean have on his computer?

	Hours	Minutes
3	**5**	**45**

Sean will have .... hour .... minutes on the computer.

7) A girl has **10 hours** revision to do. It is **12 days** before the exam. How much revision must she do each day?

She spends .... minutes each day.

	Hours	Minutes
12	**10**	

8) **8** children share a sponsored silence for a **12 hour** period. For how long must each child keep silent?

Each child keeps silent for .... hour .... minutes.

9) **6** friends play a computer game. They spend **2 hours** at the game and each has the same amount of Time playing it. How long does each one spend?

Each friend spends .... minutes playing the game.

10) **4** children work as monitors for a week in class. There are **30 hours** in total. How long is each child on duty during the week?

Each child is on duty for .... hours .... minutes.

Score

e. Months and Years

The Four Rules of Number (+ − × ÷) can be applied in a similar way to Months and Years problems.

Example:

Cathy was born in April 1995. Her cousin Alan was born **7** years **7** months earlier. When was Alan born?

We use **Base 12** for these calculations (see **Book 2** for Bases).

Subtract to find Alan's age.

Years	Months	
~~1995~~ 1994	4 + 12	
7	7	−
1987	**9**	

Borrow one year (12 months) from 1995, then follow normal Rules of Subtraction.

Alan was born in September 1987

Exercise 13: 12a Calculate the following:

1a) Harry is **5** times older than his youngest sister. If Harry is **14** years **7** months old, his sister is .... yrs .... mths.

1b) Eric's two cats are aged **3** years **6** months, **7** years **9** months. The sum of their ages is .... yrs .... mths.

1c) Shula's car was new in **June 2001** and Jane's was new in **October 2004**. The difference between the cars' ages is .... yrs .... mths.

f. Average Times

$$\text{Average Time} = \frac{\text{Sum of Times}}{\text{Number of Times}}$$

(See **Book 2** for more on Averages.)

Example:

Jeremy's arrival times at school over a **5** day period are **0906**, **0855**, **0850**, **0904** and **0845**. What is Jeremy's Mean time of arrival at school?

1. Add the times

H	M
09	06
08	55
08	50
09	04
08	45 +
44	40
2	

2. Divide by the Number of Times

$$5\,\overline{)\,44^{+240}40}$$ = **08 56**

Jeremy's Average arrival Time is **0856**

Exercise 13: 12b Calculate the following:

2. What is the Average of **3hr 14mins**, **2hr 48mins**, **1hr 57mins**, **2hr 22mins** and **1hr 54mins**? .... hr .... mins.

g. Time and Logic

Some Time questions require a logical process to solve them.
Example:

David's watch is **8 minutes** fast. At what Time (on his watch) must he start his **20 minute** journey to school if he has to be there at **8.50 a.m.**?

1. Always start with the Time given.
   David has to be at school at **8.50 a.m.**
2. Now deal with the journey first as this links to the Time given. Subtract 20 Minutes from 8.50.

   8.50 − 20mins = **8.30 a.m.**

3. Then deal with the watch. Add on 8 Minutes as his watch is fast. 8.30 + 8 Mins = **8.38 a.m.**

(-20 Mins) (+8 Mins)

8. 50 → 8. 30 → **8. 38 a.m.**

Exercise 13: 12c Calculate the following:

3) One watch is **7 minutes fast** and shows **12.15 p.m.** Another is **9 minutes slow**. What Time does the second watch show?

(-7 Mins) (Real Time) (-9 Mins)

12. 15 → .... → .... a.m.

The Time on the second watch would be .... a.m.

4) Prianka's watch is **4 minutes slow**. At what Time (on her watch) must she start her **15 minute** walk to the station to catch the **9.25 a.m.** train?

9. 25 → .... → .... a.m.

The Time on Prianka's watch would say .... a.m.

5) John's watch is **12 minutes slow** and the **7.25 a.m.** train from Heston is **15 minutes late**. What Time does John's watch say when the train eventually arrives?

7. 25 → .... → .... a.m.

The Time on John's watch would say .... a.m.

6) The **6.58 p.m.** train from Waterloo is **25 minutes late**. Luke's watch is **7 minutes fast**. What Time does Luke's watch say when the train arrives?

The Time on Luke's watch would say .... p.m.

7) The **10.08 a.m.** bus is **12 minutes early**. Rishika's watch is **5 minutes fast**. What Time does Rishika's watch say when the bus arrives?

The Time on Rishika's watch would say .... a.m.

h. Timetables

Remember when doing Timetable questions:
1. Always read and study the information carefully.
2. Read questions more than once for clear understanding.

Exercise 13: 12d

Study the train Timetable and answer the questions below:

Station	Train A	Train B	Train C	Train D
Twickenham	06:30	06:36	06:46	07:01
Richmond	06:32	06:39	06:48	---
Clapham	---	06:47	---	07:09
Vauxhall	---	06:55	06:55	---
Waterloo	06:46	07:05	07:03	07:16

8) Which train is the a) Fastest? Train ....
b) Slowest? Train ....

9a) If Naomi wants to be in Waterloo before **07:00**, which train should she catch? Train ....

9b) Which train is fastest from Richmond to Waterloo? Train .... is the fastest.

10a) Paul misses the **06:30** train to Waterloo and might be late for work. Should he catch **Train B** or **Train C** to Waterloo? He should catch Train ....

10b) Natalie works at Waterloo and travels from Twickenham. What is the difference in arrival Time for **Train B** and **Train C**? The difference is .... minutes.

Score

i. Time Zones

The world is Divided into a number of Time Zones:
To find different Times in other parts of the world Additions or Subtractions are made to London Time.

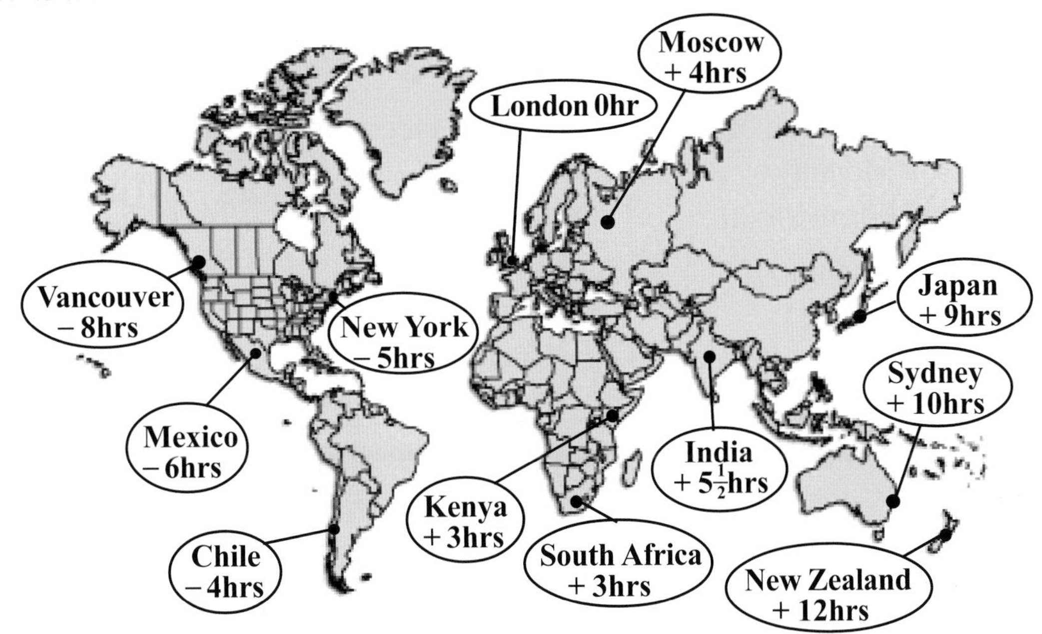

Example: If it is **0400** in England, what Time is it in Japan?

Japan is 9 hours in front of London. Simply Add 9 hours to the London Time. **0400 + 9 hours = 1300 hours**.

Exercise 13: 13 Give your Answers in the same format as the question ie. in either 12 or 24 hour time.

Score

When it is **0900** in London, what Time is it in:

1) New York .... 2) Kenya .... 3) Chile ....

4) When it is **23:30** in Sydney what Time is it in London?

....

5) If it is **5.00 p.m.** in South Africa what Time would it be in Moscow? ....

When it is **Midnight** in London it is: 6) .... in India
7) .... in Mexico 8) .... in Vancouver.

When it is **Midday** in New Zealand it is:
9) .... in London 10) .... in Sydney.

j. Mixed Examples

Exercise 13: 14 Calculate the following:

1) A woman is in hospital from **9.30 a.m.** on Monday until **5.15 p.m.** on Thursday. How long does she stay there?

To find the length of Time on Monday, **Subtract** from 24:00.

Hours	Minutes
24	**00**
9	**30** –

Add the Hours up from all the days.

	Hours	Minutes
Monday	....	....
Tuesday	....	....
Wednesday	....	....
Thursday	....	....

She stays ...... days, ... hours and ...... mins in hospital.

2) A football game lasting **90 minutes** started at **2.30 p.m.** If the half-time break lasted **15 minutes** and there were **6 minutes** of injury time added on, at what Time did the game finish?

The game finished at .... p.m.

3) A factory worker on night shift starts at **7.30 p.m.** and finishes at **6.15 a.m.** How many Hours does he work a week if he works **4** nights?

He works .... hours .... minutes.

4) The **19:15** flight from New York to London Heathrow lands **35 minutes** early. Joanna's watch is **22 minutes** fast. What Time does her watch say when the aeroplane lands at Heathrow?

The watch says .... (write in 24 Hour Clock).

5) A hovercraft leaves Dover at **14:23** and arrives at Calais at **16:12**. How long was the journey? (in English Time).

The journey was .... hour and .... minutes.

Study the timetable and answer the questions.

Coaches	**A**	**B**	**C**
London Central	06:35	08:26	10:20
Gatwick Airport	07:49	10:09	11:33
Time Taken	**1hr 14mins**	....	....

6) How long do **Coaches B** and **C** take to do the journey?
Coach B takes .... hour .... minutes.
Coach C takes .... hour .... minutes.

7) If I wanted to arrive promptly for a flight check-in Time of **11:15 a.m.**, which coach would I need to catch?

I would need to catch Coach ....

---

8) Danny sleeps from **9.30 p.m.** until **7.30 a.m.** What Fraction of a Day does he spend in bed?

The Fraction of the Day is ....

9) **3** playing pairs share Time equally on a tennis court. They play for **1 hour 45 minutes**. How long does each couple play for? They play for .... minutes each.

10) Work out how many Hours and Minutes there are between **14:23** on Wednesday and **23:57** on Friday.
There are .... hours .... minutes.

Score

6. Time, Distance, Speed

The Formulae for finding Time, Distance and Speed are:

$$\textbf{Time} = \frac{\text{Distance}}{\text{Speed}} \qquad \textbf{Speed} = \frac{\text{Distance}}{\text{Time}}$$

$$\textbf{Distance} = \text{Speed} \times \text{Time}$$

They can be represented by the **Formula Triangle** below:

Learn as an **Aid to Memory**.

The 3 elements are **Alphabetical** in an **Anti-clockwise Direction**.

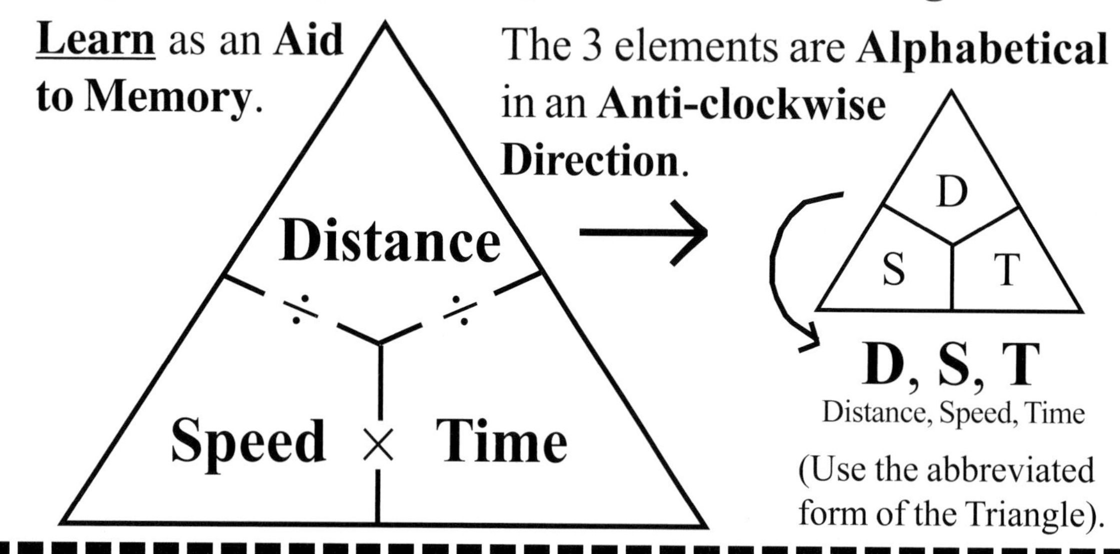

D, S, T
Distance, Speed, Time

(Use the abbreviated form of the Triangle).

a. Finding (Average) Speed

An object travelling at the same Speed all the time has **Uniform** or **Steady Speed**. Most things (trains, people aeroplanes etc. do not travel at Uniform Speed, but we can still find their **Average Speed** using this Formula.

Example: A car travels **160km** in **4 hours**. What is the Average Speed?

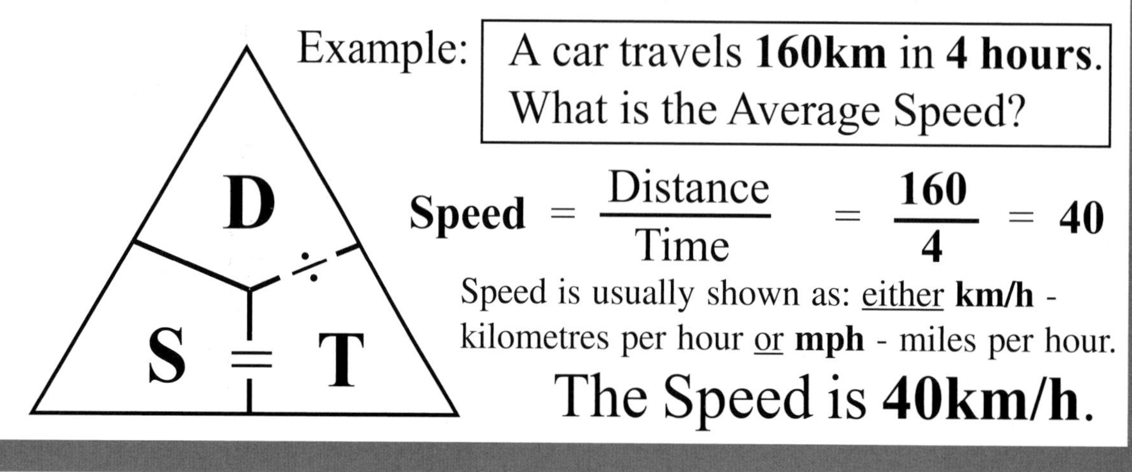

$$\textbf{Speed} = \frac{\text{Distance}}{\text{Time}} = \frac{\mathbf{160}}{\mathbf{4}} = \mathbf{40}$$

Speed is usually shown as: <u>either</u> **km/h** - kilometres per hour <u>or</u> **mph** - miles per hour.

The Speed is **40km/h**.

Exercise 13: 15a Calculate the following:

1) A coach journey of **480km** takes **6 hours**. Find the Average Speed in km/h.

The Average Speed is .... km/h.

2) A boy goes on a sponsored walk. He walks **20 miles** and it takes **5 hours**. What is the Average Speed in mph?

The Average Speed is .... mph.

If the question involves Minutes it is best to change them to parts of an Hour and Divide or Multiply in Fractions.

Example:

A train journey of **228km** takes **1 Hour 54 Minutes**. Find the Average Speed in km/h.

1. **Convert** 1hr 54 Mins into Fractions of an Hour. (60 + 54 mins = 114 mins) $= \frac{114}{60}$

2. **Express** the Distance as a Fraction. $= \frac{228}{1}$

3. **Formula:** **Speed** $= \frac{\text{Distance}}{\text{Time}}$

or **Speed** = Distance ÷ Time

$$\underset{\text{Distance}}{\frac{228}{1}} \div \underset{\text{Time}}{\frac{114}{60}}$$

4. **Divide** as a **Fraction** (see **Book 2**)
   - Invert 2nd Fraction/change sign to Times
   - Cancel and Multiply out
   - If it is an Improper Fraction - Divide
   - Simplify if necessary

$$\frac{\overset{2}{\cancel{228}}}{1} \times \frac{60}{\underset{1}{\cancel{114}}}$$

$$\frac{2}{1} \times \frac{60}{1}$$

The train travels at **120km/h**.

Exercise 13: 15b Calculate the following:

3) A girl walks **$4\frac{1}{2}$miles** to school. It takes her **90 minutes**.

Her Average Speed is .... mph. $\frac{9}{2} \div \frac{90}{60}$

4) An aeroplane journey of **480km** takes **40 minutes**. Find the Average Speed in km/h.

The Average Speed is .... km/h.

b. Finding a Time

The Time can be found using the Formula:

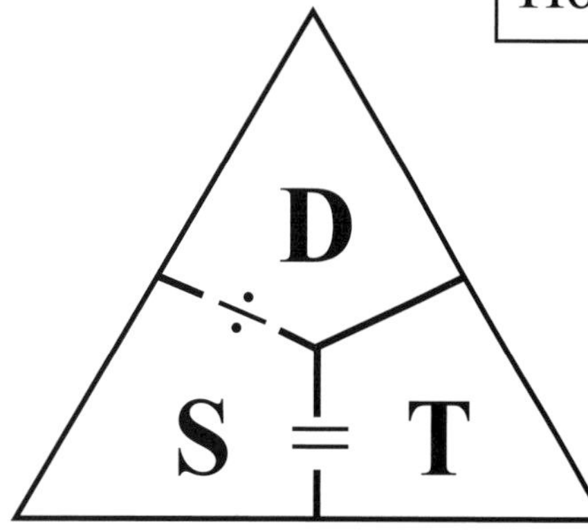

Example:

A car travels at **40km/h** for **160km**
How long does the journey take?

$$\textbf{Time} = \frac{\text{Distance}}{\text{Speed}}$$

$$= \frac{160}{40} = 4$$

It is a **4 Hour** journey.

Exercise 13: 15c Calculate the following:

5) A coach travelled **4,800km** across Europe at an Average Speed of **60km/h**. How long did the journey take?

The journey took .... hours. $\textbf{Time} = \frac{D}{S} = \frac{4800}{60}$

6) A car travels at an Average Speed of **60mph**. How long will it take to travel **360 miles**?

It will take .... hours.

Questions can require Conversions to Minutes.

Example:

A boy cycles at **12mph**. How long will it take him to cycle **8 miles**?

Time $= \frac{D}{S} = \frac{8}{12}$

The answer will be a Fraction of an Hour so Multiply by **60** to **Convert to Minutes**.

$\frac{8}{{}_1\cancel{12}} \times \frac{\cancel{60}^5}{1}$

Cancel/Simplify/Multiply out.

$\frac{8}{1} \times \frac{5}{1} = 40$

It will take the boy **40 Minutes**.

Exercise 13: 15d Calculate the following:

7) A motorbike travels at an Average Speed of **64mph**. How long will it take to travel **16 miles**?

$\frac{16}{64} \times \frac{60}{1}$

The journey will take .... mins.

8) A girl cycles home from school at an Average Speed of **12km/h**. If she has to cycle **5km**, how long will it take?

The journey will take .... mins.

c. Finding a Distance

Use Formula to find Distance:

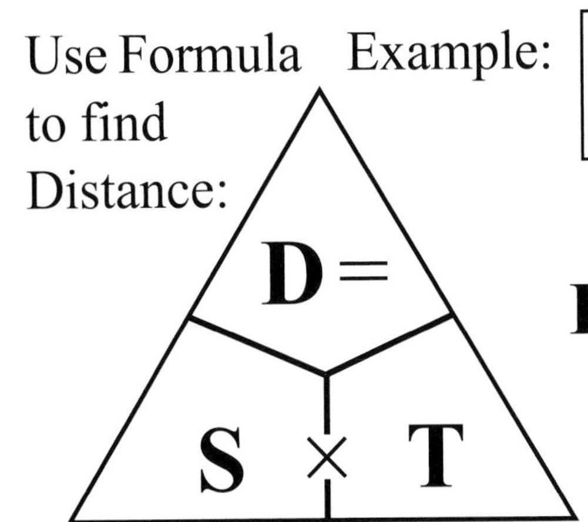

Example:

A car travels at **30km/h** for **2 Hours**. How far does it travel?

Distance = Speed × Time

Distance $= 30 \times 2$

$= 60$

The car travels **60km**.

Sometimes it is necessary to Multiply by parts of an Hour.
Example:

A boy runs at **5mph** for **1 Hour 12 Minutes**. How far does he run?

1. **Express** the Speed as a Fraction. $= \frac{5}{1}$

2. **Convert** 1 hr 12 mins into Fractions of an Hour. (60 + 12mins = 72mins) $= \frac{72}{60}$

3. **Formula:**

Distance = Speed × Time $\qquad \frac{\cancel{5}^{1}}{1} \times \frac{\cancel{72}^{6}}{\cancel{60}_{\cancel{12}\,1}}$

The boy runs for **6 Miles.**

Exercise 13: 15e Calculate the following:

9) A train travels at **84mph**. How far would it travel in **5 minutes**?

The train will travel .... miles. $\frac{84}{1} \times \frac{5}{60}$

10) An athlete runs a marathon at an Average Speed of **15km/h**. He completes the marathon in **3 hours**. How far does he run? He runs .... km.

Score

d. Mixed Examples

Exercise 13: 16 Calculate the following:

1) A car travels **155 miles** in $2\frac{1}{2}$ **hours**. Find the Average Speed.

Speed $= \frac{\text{Distance}}{\text{Time}}$ $\qquad \frac{155}{1} \div \frac{5}{2}$

The Average Speed of the car is .... mph.

2) A car travels **12 miles** at an Average Speed of **30mph**. How long does the journey take?

$$\textbf{Time} = \frac{\text{Distance}}{\text{Speed}} \qquad \text{Divide } \frac{12}{30} \times \frac{60}{1} \text{ Multiply to give Minutes}$$

The journey takes .... minutes.

3) A man rows at **12km/h**. He rows for **45 minutes**. How far does he row?

$$\textbf{Distance} = \text{Speed} \times \text{Time} \qquad \frac{12}{1} \times \frac{45}{60}$$

The man rows .... km.

4) What is the Average Speed of a car, if it covers a Distance of **40km** in **50 minutes**? The speed is .... km/h.

5) Vicky walks at an Average Speed of **8km/h**. How far will she travel in **$3\frac{3}{4}$ hours**? She will travel .... km.

6) Travelling at **40mph**, how long will it take to travel **120 miles**? It will take .... hours.

7) A coach travels **4600km**. If it was driven at **50km/h**, how long did the journey take? It took .... hours.

8-10) This is a table of air flights. Fill in the missing information on the table.

	Distance	Time	Average Speed
8)	**2400 miles**	**3hrs**	.... mph
9)	**3840 miles**	.... hrs	**960mph**
10)	.... miles	**3hrs 20mins**	**1200mph**

Score

Chapter Fourteen

SYMMETRY

1. Reflective Symmetry

Some Shapes can be split in half so that each half looks exactly the same. One side is a mirror Reflection of the other side. The Line acts like a mirror creating a Reflection called the **Line** (or **Axis**) **of Symmetry**. The Shapes below have **Reflective Symmetry** or **Line Symmetry**.

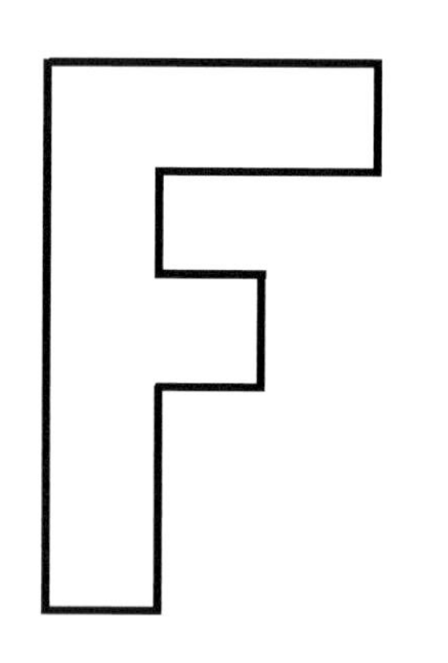

This Shape has **no Lines of Symmetry**. It is said to be **Asymmetrical**.

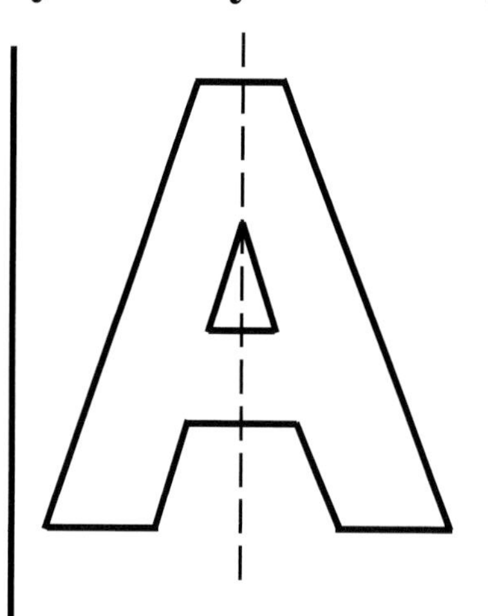

This Shape has only **one Line (Axis) of Symmetry**.

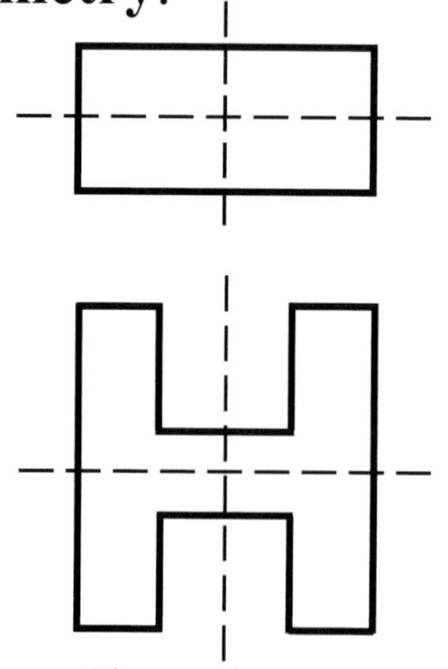

These Shapes have **two Lines (Axes) of Symmetry**.

Exercise 14: 1 Answer the following:

A B C D E F G H I J K L M

N O P Q R S T U V W X Y Z

1) Which capital letters have a <u>Horizontal</u> Line of Symmetry? ....

2) Which capital letters have a <u>Vertical</u> Line of Symmetry? ....

3) Which letters are Asymmetrical? ....

Write how many Lines of Symmetry these Shapes have?

4) ....

5) ....

6) .... It has more than 2 Lines of Symmetry.

Finish these Shapes using the Lines of Symmetry.

7)

8)

9)

10) Draw in the Lines of Symmetry on these Shapes.

Score

2. Rotational Symmetry

A Shape has Rotational Symmetry if it can be turned round at its **Centre** onto different positions that look exactly alike. A **360°** turn is one **Revolution** or **Complete Rotation**.

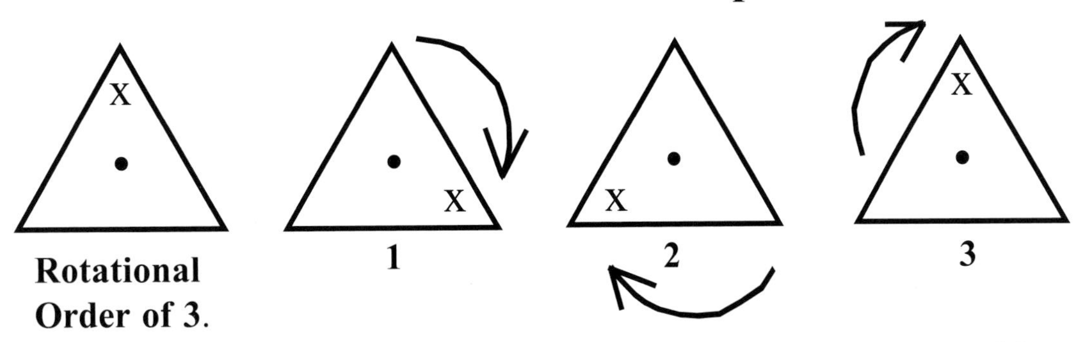

Rotational Order of 3.

The triangle can be turned 3 times and placed on itself to look the same as its original position (x shows the moves).

Every Shape has an **Order of Rotational Symmetry**.

Even a Shape that can only be Rotated on itself once has a Rotational Order.

Hence the F Shape has an **Order of Rotational Symmetry of 1**.

However, Shapes with an Order of Rotational Symmetry of 1 are said to have **No Rotational Symmetry**.

Example:

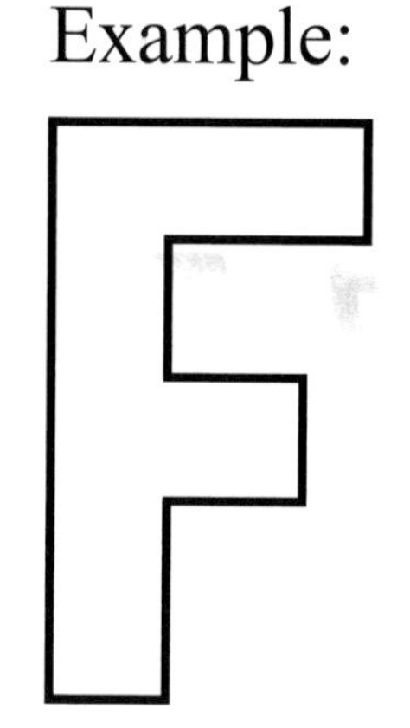

Exercise 14: 2

Write the Order of Rotational Symmetry for the following:

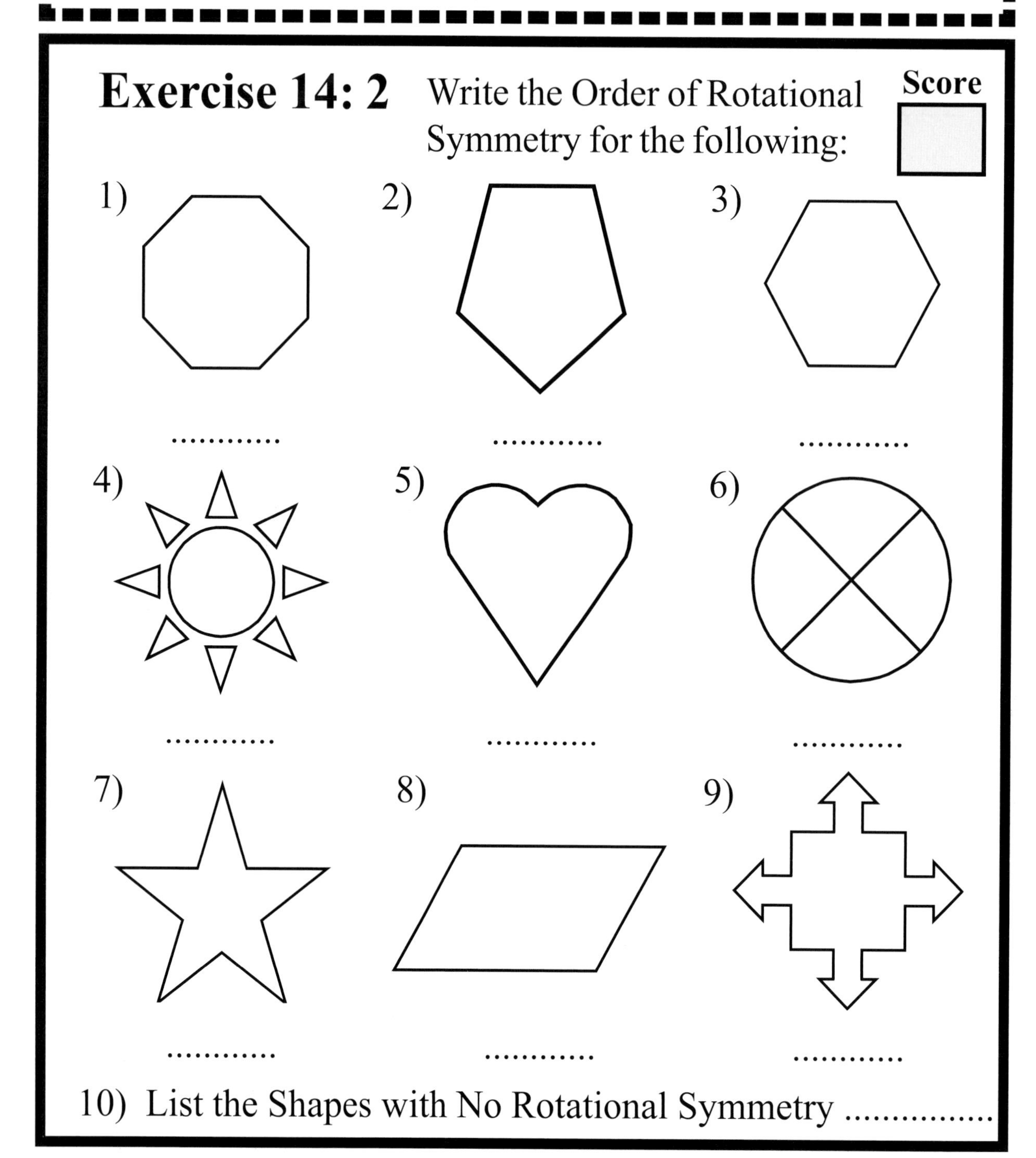

10) List the Shapes with No Rotational Symmetry ....

Chapter Fifteen

SHAPES

1. Two Dimensional Shapes

a. Triangles (Three Sided Shapes)

To help with learning two dimensional shapes, think about:

Angles **Sides** **Rotation** **Reflection**

Equilateral

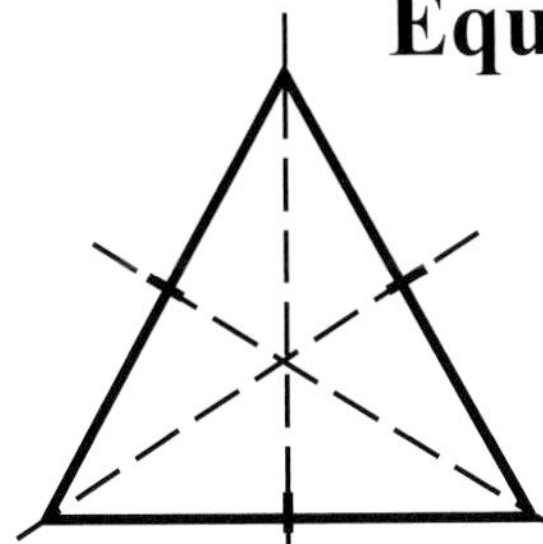

- Rotational Symmetry of 3.
- Line Symmetry of 3.
- 3 Equal Sides.
- 3 Equal Angles (60°).

Isosceles

- No Rotational Symmetry.
- Line Symmetry of 1.
- 2 Equal Sides.
- 2 Equal Angles.

Scalene

- No Rotational Symmetry.
- Asymmetrical; no Line Symmetry.
- No Equal Sides.
- No Equal Angles.

Right Angle (Scalene)

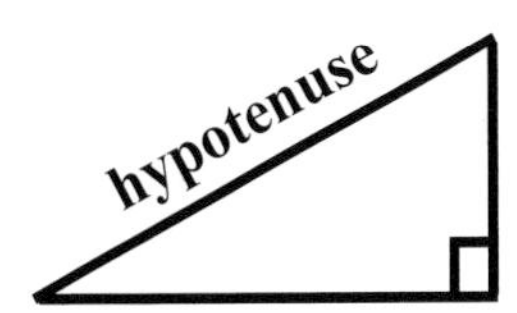

- Same qualities as a Scalene Triangle.
- One 90° Angle.
- The Hypotenuse is the longest side.

Right Angle (Isosceles)

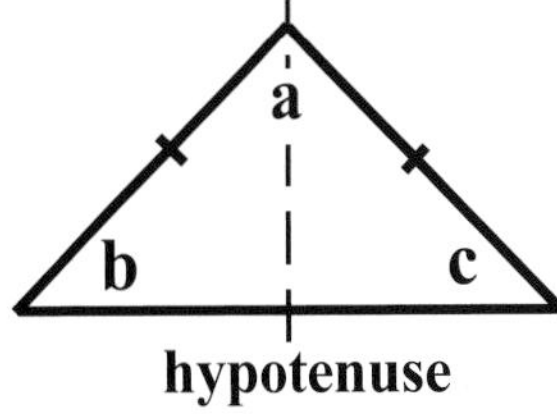

hypotenuse

- Same qualities as an Isosceles Triangle.
- Two 45° Angles (**b** & **c**) and one 90° Angle (**a**).

Acute

- None of the Angles is greater than 90°.
- Can be Isosceles, Equilateral, or Scalene (Scalene **can** have Angles greater than 90° as above).

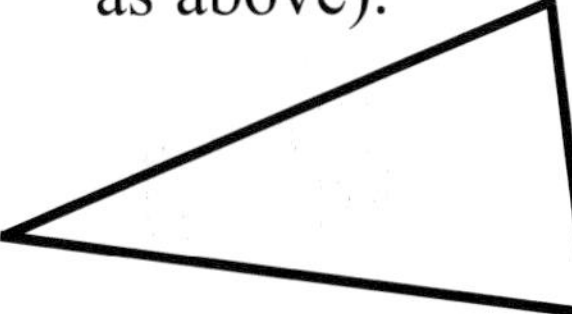

Obtuse

- One Angle greater than 90° (Angle **a**).
- It is either Scalene or Isosceles.

a

The Median

The Median is a straight Line **AB** drawn from the tip of the Triangle to the middle of the Opposite Side.

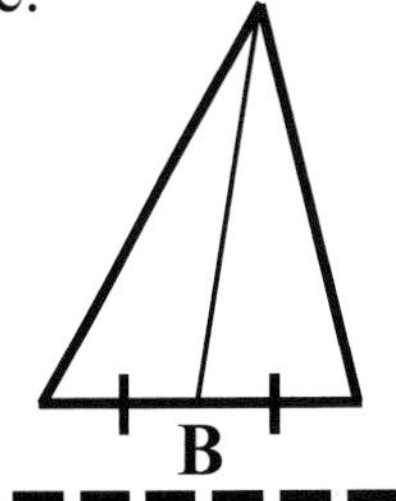

Exercise 15: 1a Answer the following:

1) List the types of Triangles that have No Rotational Symmetry. ....

2) Is this Triangle Acute or Obtuse?
   a) The Triangle is ....
   b) The Line AB is called a ....

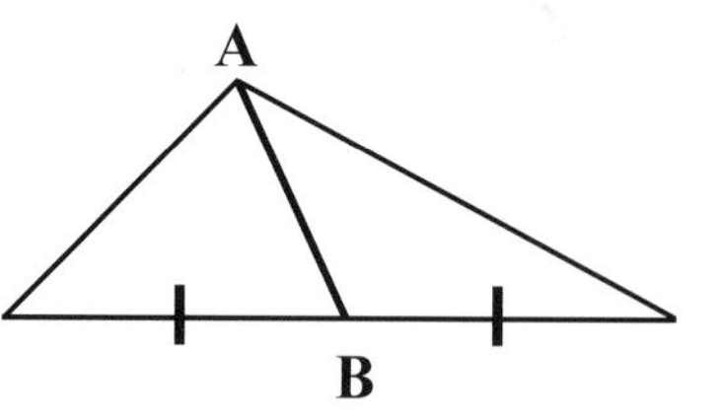

3) a) If AB = AC, this is an .... Triangle.
   b) It has .... Line(s) of Symmetry.
   c) It has an Order of Rotation of ....

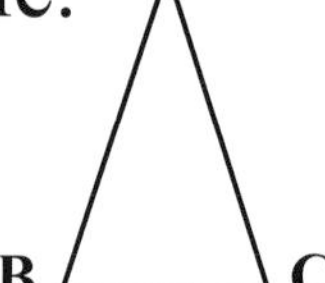

4) a) Which Triangle has Equal Sides? ....
   b) Each Angle is ....°

5) a) What types of Triangles never have Equal Sides or Angles? ....
   b) These Triangles have a Rotational Order of ....

b. Quadrilaterals (Four Sided Shapes)

Rectangles

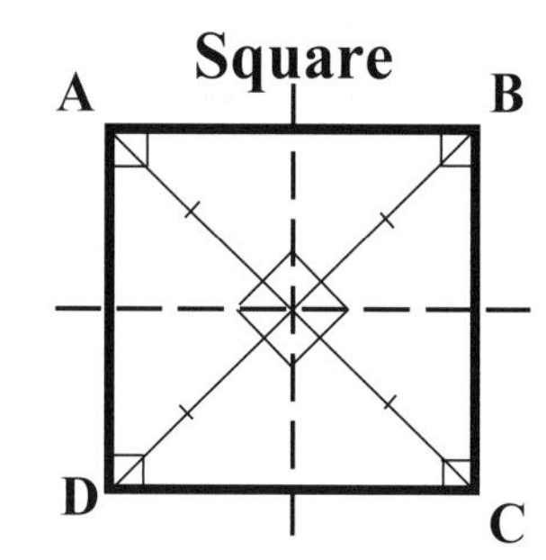

- 4 Equal Sides.
- 4 Equal Angles of 90°.
- Rotational symmetry of 4.
- Line Symmetry of 4.
- Diagonals AC & BD Bisect each other at Right Angles.

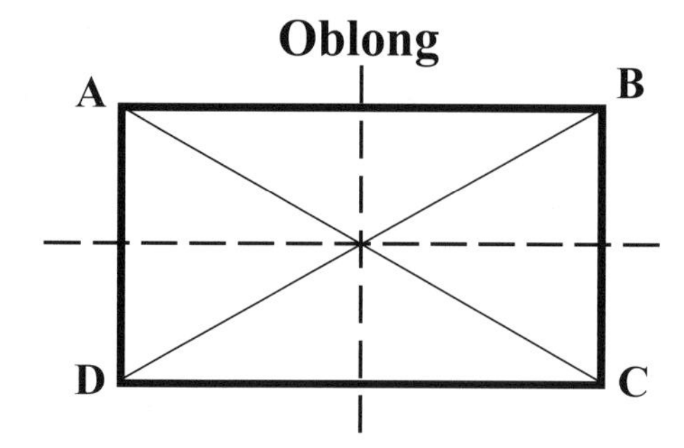

- 2 pairs of Equal Sides.
- 4 Equal Angles of 90°.
- Rotational Symmetry of 2.
- Line Symmetry of 2.
- Diagonals AC & BD are Equal.
- Diagonals AC & BD Bisect.

Parallelogram

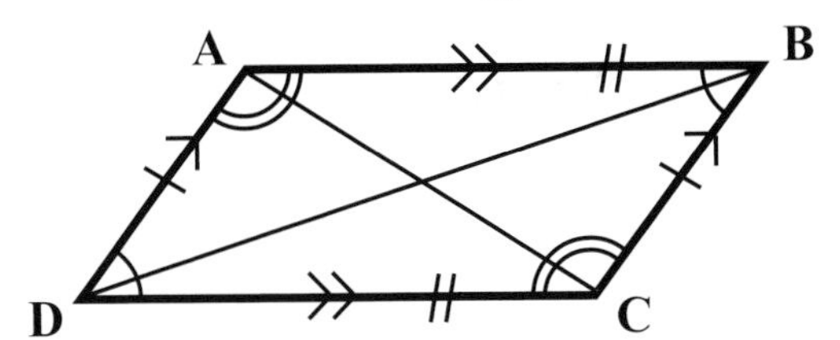

- 2 pairs of Parallel Equal Sides.
- Opposite Angles are Equal.
- No Line Symmetry.
- Rotational Symmetry of 2.
- Diagonals AC & BD Bisect.
- Diagonals AC & BD are not Equal.

Rhombus
(plural: **Rhombi**)

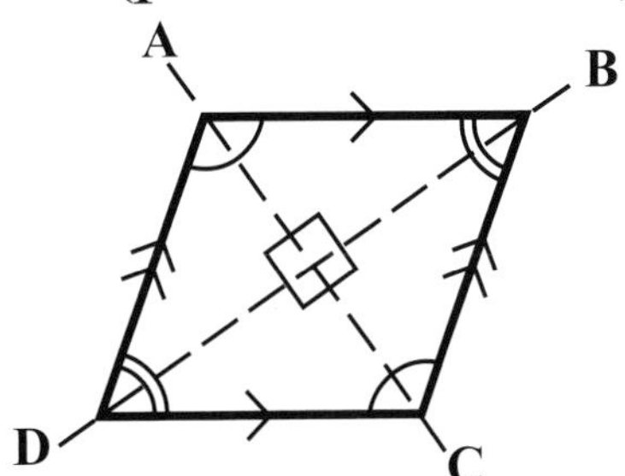

(This is a special type of Parallelogram.)
- All four Sides of Equal length.
- 2 pairs of Parallel Sides.
- 2 pairs of Opposite Equal Angles.
- Line Symmetry of 2.
- Rotational Symmetry of 2.
- Diagonals AC & BD Bisect each other at Right Angles.

Kite

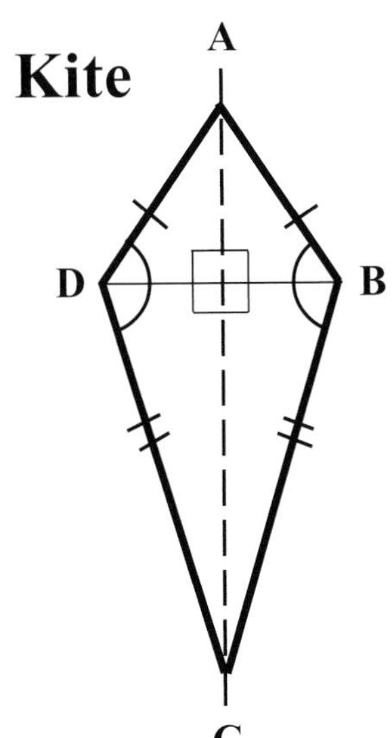

- 2 pairs of Adjacent Equal Sides.
- 1 pair of Equal Angles.
- No Rotational Symmetry.
- Line Symmetry of 1.
- Diagonal AC Bisects BD at Right Angles.

Trapezium
(plural: **Trapezia**)

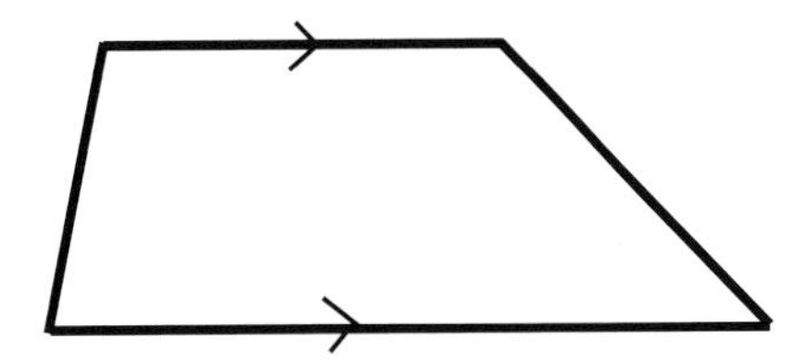

- 2 Parallel Sides of Unequal Length.
- 4 Angles, 2 of which can be the same size.
- Asymmetrical; no Line Symmetry.
- No Rotational Symmetry.

Isosceles Trapezium

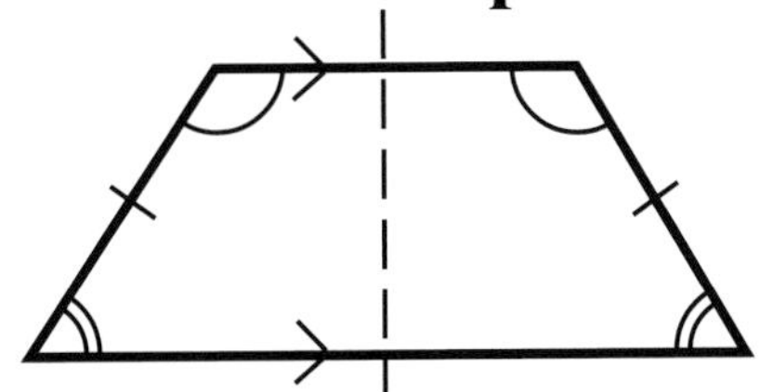

(This is a special type of Trapezium.)
- 2 Parallel Sides of Unequal length.
- 2 Sides of Equal length.
- 2 pairs of Angles of the same size.
- Line Symmetry of 1.
- No Rotational Symmetry.

Arrowhead

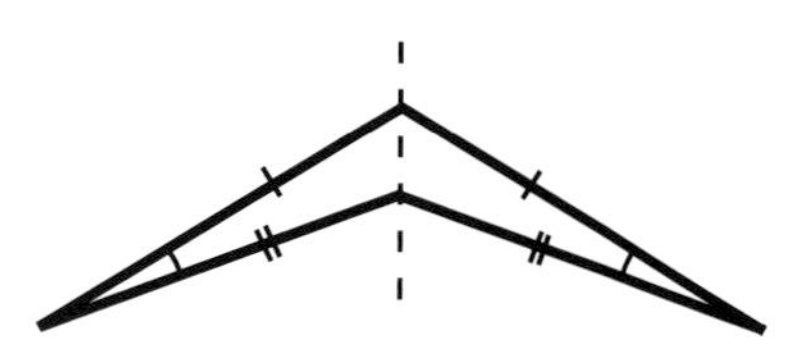

- 2 pairs of Adjacent Equal Sides.
- 1 pair of Equal Angles.
- Line Symmetry of 1.
- No Rotational Symmetry.

Irregular Quadrilateral

All other four-sided shapes are simply referred to as Irregular Quadrilaterals. They do not fit into any other group.

- No Line Symmetry.
- No Rotational Symmetry.
- No Equal Angles.
- No Equal Sides.

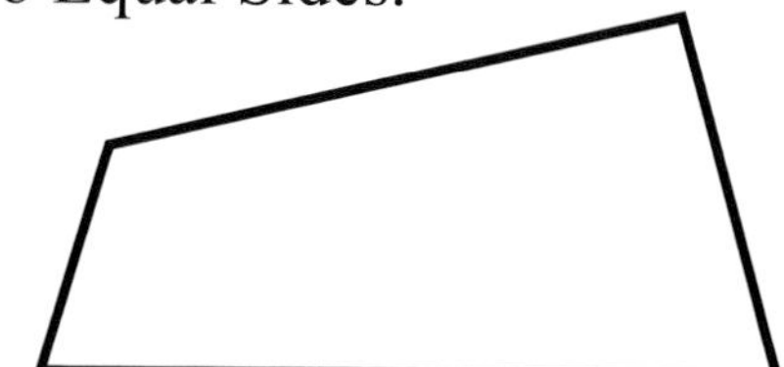

Pentomino

A shape made from 5 squares.

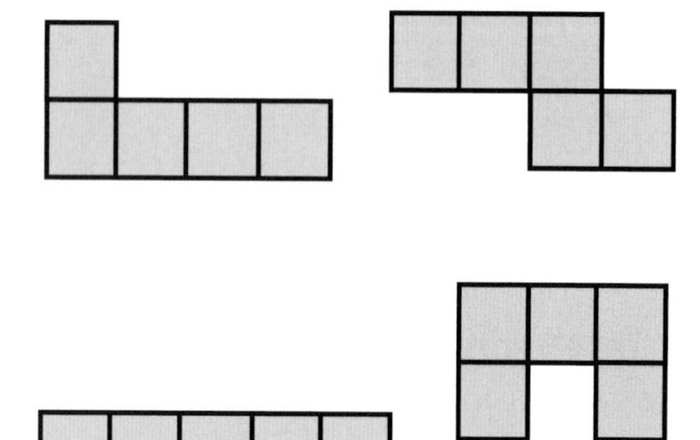

Hexomino

A shape made from 6 squares.

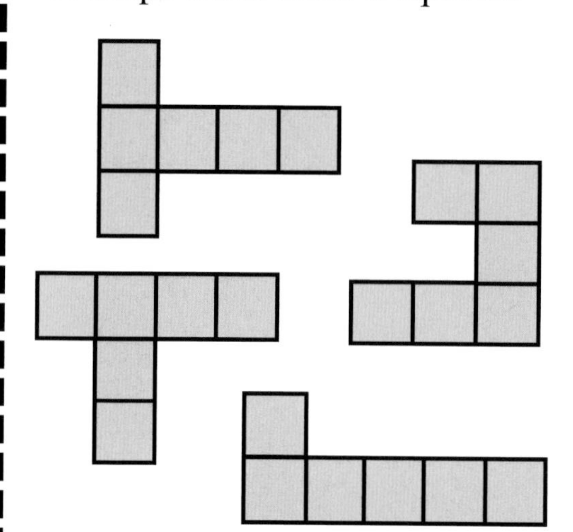

Exercise 15: 1b Answer the following:

6) What 4-sided Shapes have one Line of Symmetry?
   a) .... b) ....
   c) ....

7) Name a Quadrilateral that has only one pair of Equal Angles and one Line of Symmetry. ....

8) a) Draw in Lines of Reflective Symmetry.
   b) This Shape is a ....

9) A .... can have 4 Unequal Sides, of which none is parallel, and 4 unequal Angles.

10) a) What Quadrilateral has two Parallel Sides, but is Asymmetrical? ....

b) This Quadrilateral is Asymmetrical with Sloping Parallel Sides ....

Score

c. Polygona (Many Sided Shapes)

'Poly' means Many and 'gon' means Angled. A 'Polygon' is a Many Angled/Sided Shape (usually more than four Sides).

All **Regular Polygona (Polygons)** have the same pattern of properties. All the shapes have Equal Sides and Equal Angles. Rotational and Reflective Symmetry corresponds to the number of Equal Sides and Equal Angles. e.g. The Pentagon has 5 of each property, the Hexagon 6 etc.

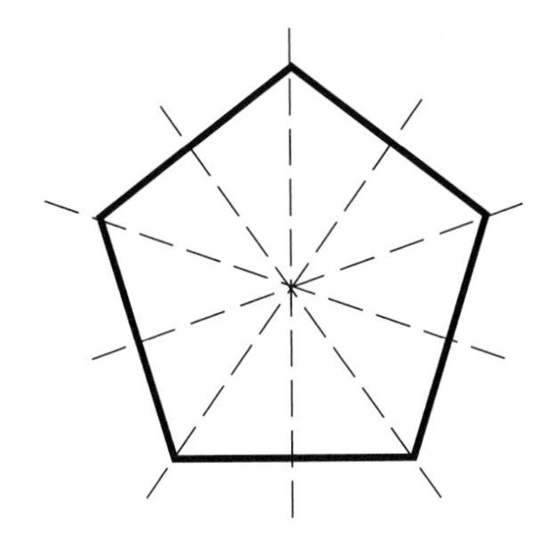

Regular Pentagon

- 5 Equal Sides.
- 5 Equal Angles.
- Rotational Symmetry of 5.
- Line Symmetry of 5.

Regular Hexagon (6 Equal Sides)

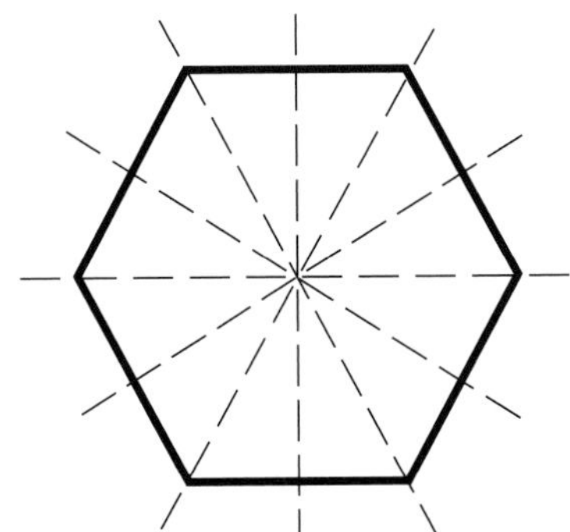

Regular Heptagon (7 Equal Sides)

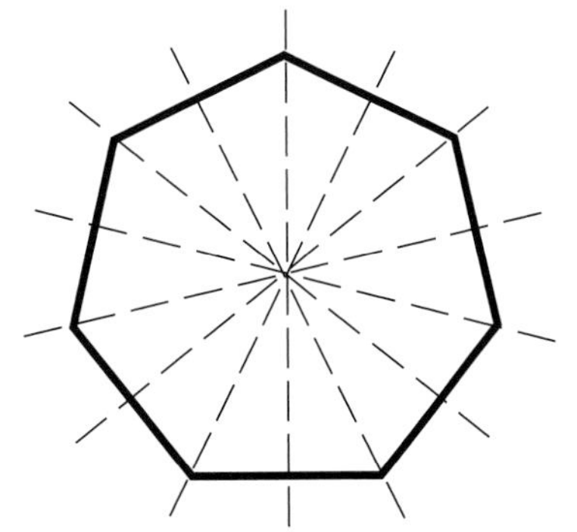

Regular Octagon (8 Equal Sides)

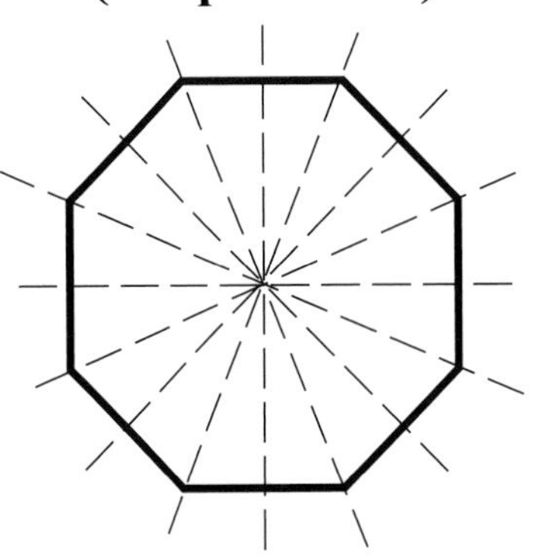

Regular Nonagon (9 Equal Sides)

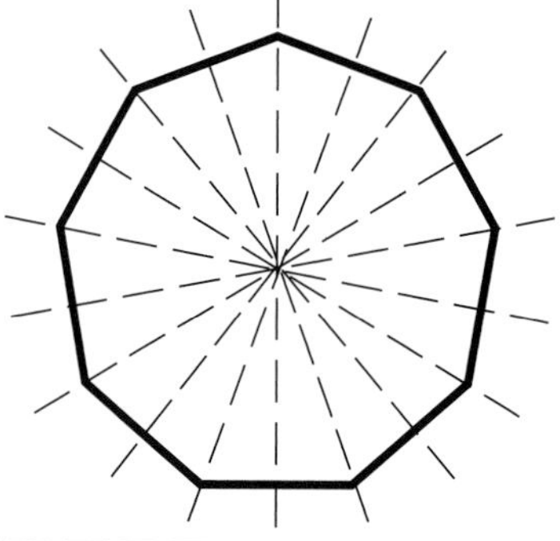

Regular Decagon (10 Equal Sides)

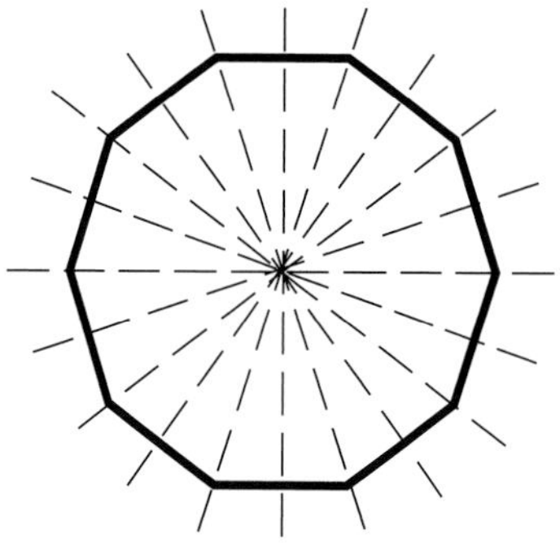

Regular Dodecagon (12 Equal Sides)

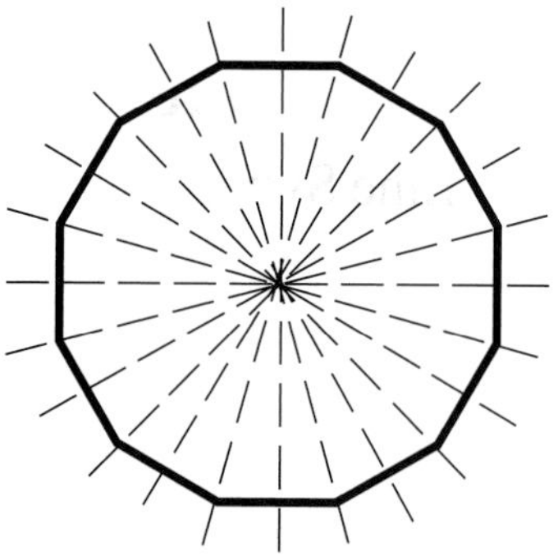

Other Polygona

Hendecagon (11 Sides).

Quindecagon (15 Sides).

Icosagon (20 Sides).

Irregular Polygona

All Polygons which are not regular are termed **Irregular**.

Example:

Irregular Hexagon

This Irregular Polygon is Asymmetrical (no Line or Rotational Symmetry) and has no Equal Sides or Angles.

Exercise 15: 2a

1) Name these Shapes: a) 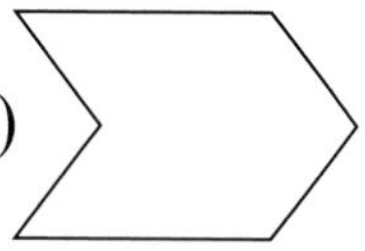 b)  c)

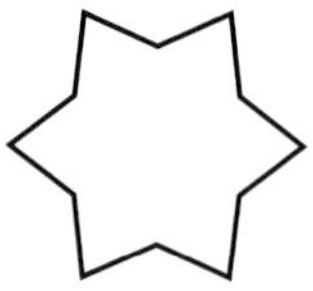

a) .... b) .... c) ....

2) Write how many Axes of Symmetry each Shape has.

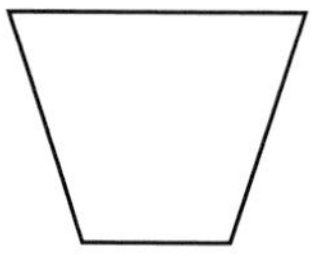

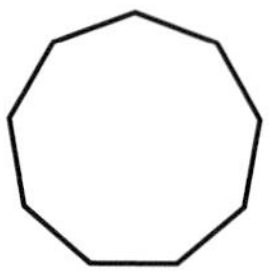

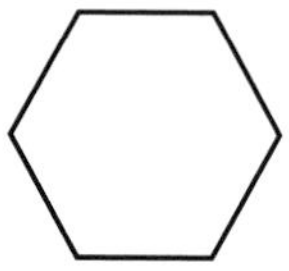

....

3) List 3 Regular Polygons that have <u>No</u> Parallel Sides.

....

4) How many of the following Shapes have at least one pair of Parallel Sides? .... Shapes.

Regular Hexagon Irregular Decagon Regular Pentagon
Isosceles Trapezium Equilateral Triangle Rhombus

5) Write the Order of Rotation under each of these Shapes.

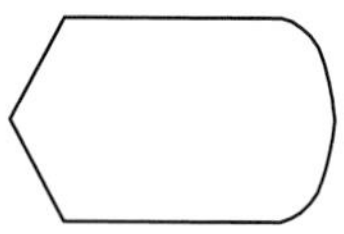

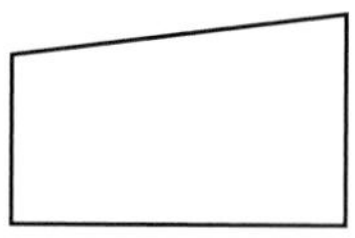

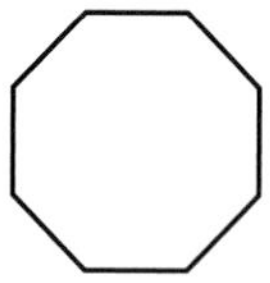

....

d. Circular Shapes

Circle

- Line Symmetry infinite (endless).
- Rotational Symmetry infinite (endless).

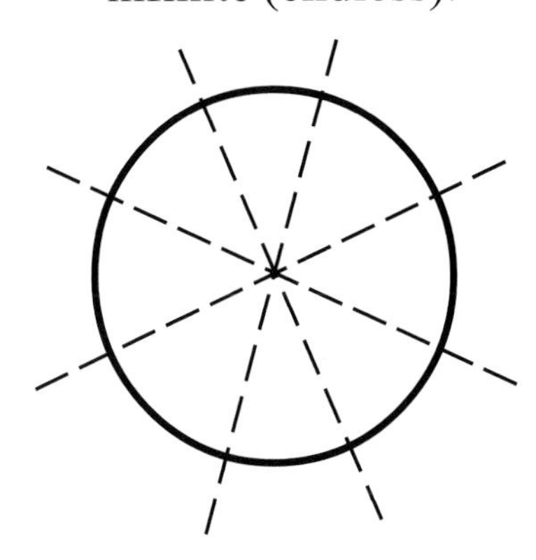

Circle Measurements

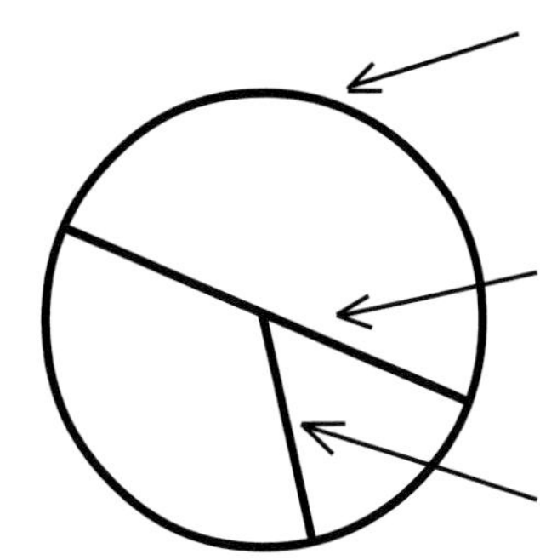

Circumference
Perimeter - Distance all the way round.

Diameter
Line across full width of Circle (passes through the Centre).

Radius
A Line halfway across (from the Centre to the edge). Radii is plural (more than one).

Concentric Circles

Circles with the same point at the centre.

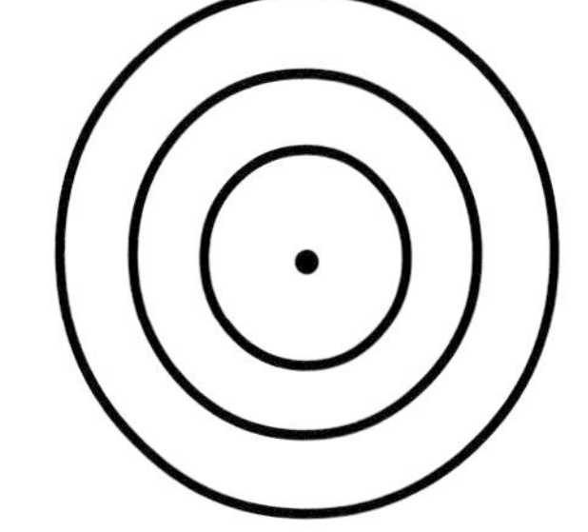

Annulus

A ring formed by 2 Concentric Circles.

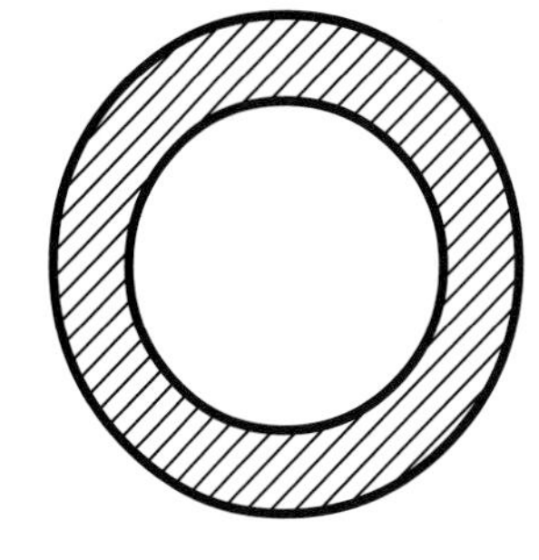

Semi-circle

A half Circle.

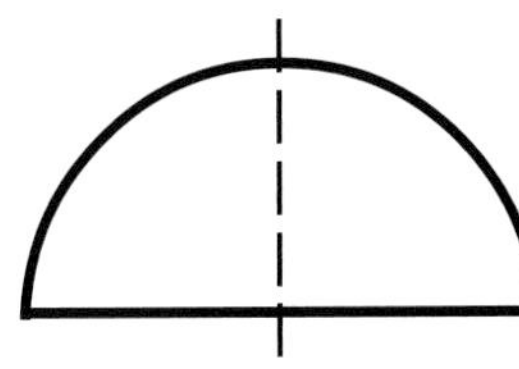

- No Rotational Symmetry.
- Line Symmetry of 1.

Chord

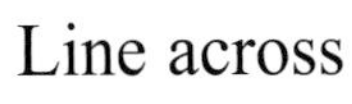

Line across a Circle.

Arc

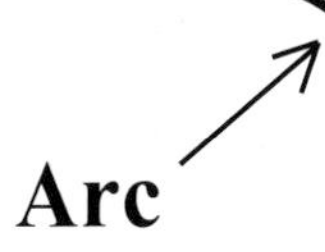

Part of the Circumference of a Circle.

Ellipse

An Oval Shape.

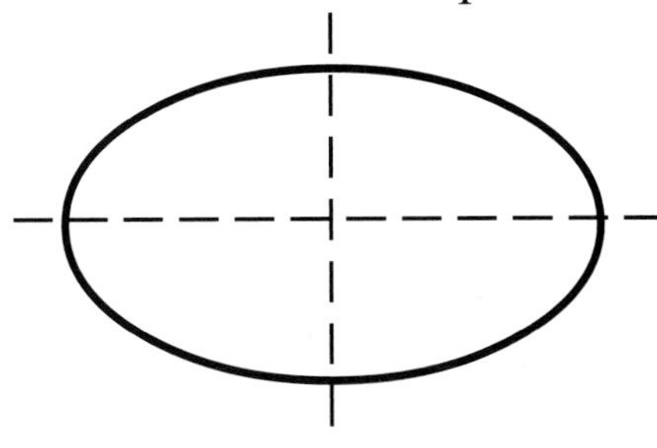

- Rotational Symmetry of 2.
- Line Symmetry of 2.

Tangent

A straight Line that touches the Circumference of the Circle in one place only.

Parabola

If a ball is hit or thrown it makes a curved shape called a Parabola as it travels through the air.

Sector

A Fraction of a Circle.

Segment

A piece created by a Chord.

Quadrant

A Quarter.

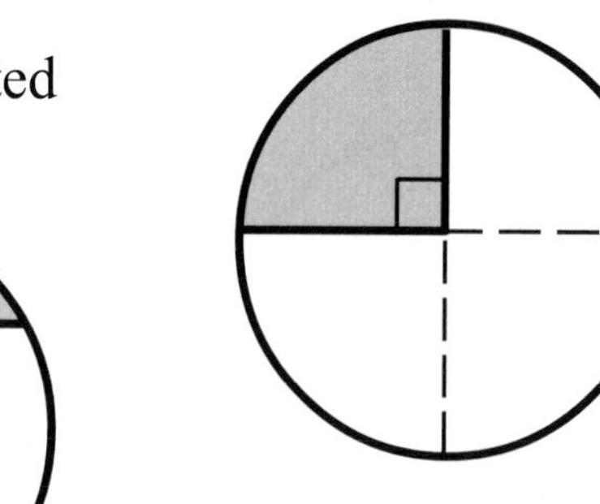

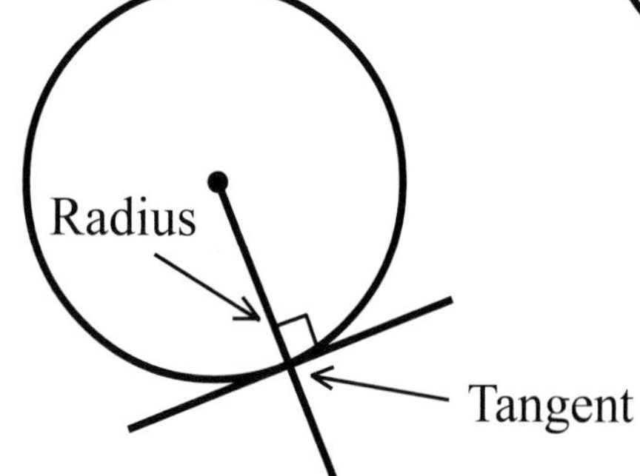

The Radius and Tangent at a point make an angle of 90°.

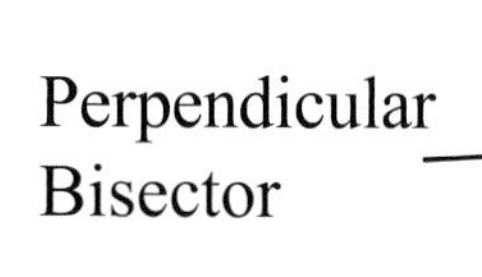

The Perpendicular Bisector of a chord passes through the centre of a circle.

Exercise 15: 2b Answer the following:

6) a) The Line across is a ....
   b) The Line halfway across is a ....
   c) The Perimeter is called a ....

7) a) The Rotational Order for this Shape is ....
   b) How many Lines of Reflective Symmetry? ....

8) a) What is this Shape called? ....
   b) What is the Order of Rotational Symmetry?
   ....

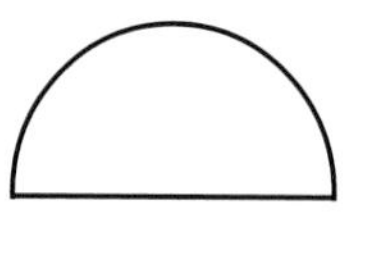

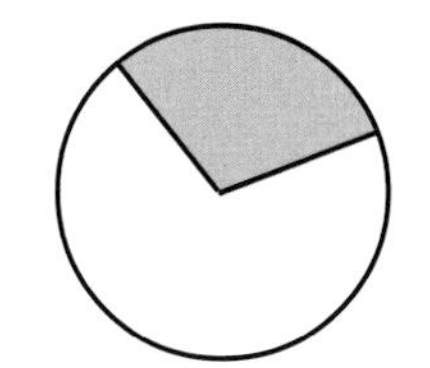

9) a) This is called a ....
b) If it were made into one quarter of the Circle it would be called a ....

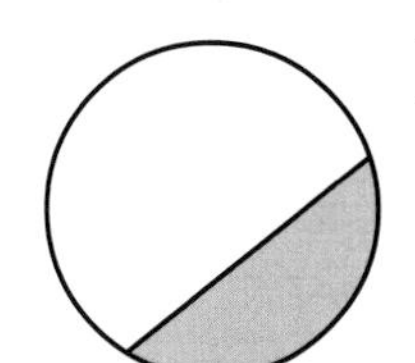

10) a) The shaded area is called a ....
b) The line that Divides up the Circle is called a ....

Score

2. Shapes and Angles

a. Describing Shapes and Angles

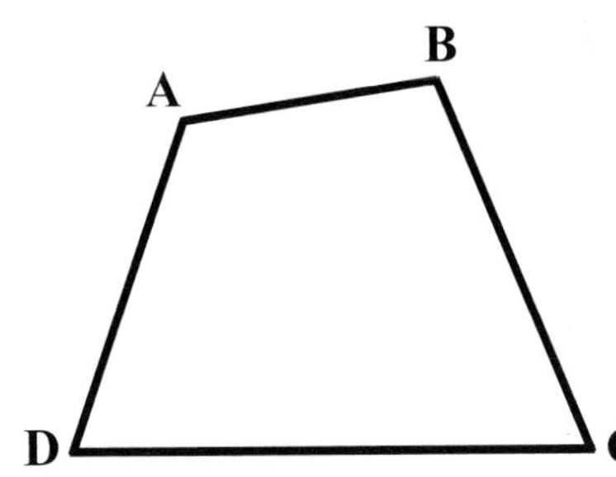

Each corner of this Shape is called a **Vertex**. The Shape ABCD has 4 **Vertices**. Each Side is termed by the two letters of each Vertex. It has 4 Sides AB, BC, CD and AD.

Each Angle can be described in 3 different ways:

1. Use a lower case (small) letter - **a**
2. Use the Vertex upper case (capital) letter with a 'hat' - $\hat{A}$
3. Use the 2 Sides that form the Angle - $D\hat{A}B$ **or** $B\hat{A}D$

b. Triangles

The Interior (inside) Angles of a Triangle Add up to 180°.

'Angle Chasing' is the process of having to find one or more other Angles before being able to calculate the required Angle.

Finding an Interior (inside) Angle of a Triangle.

Example 1: Find **Angle a** in this Triangle.

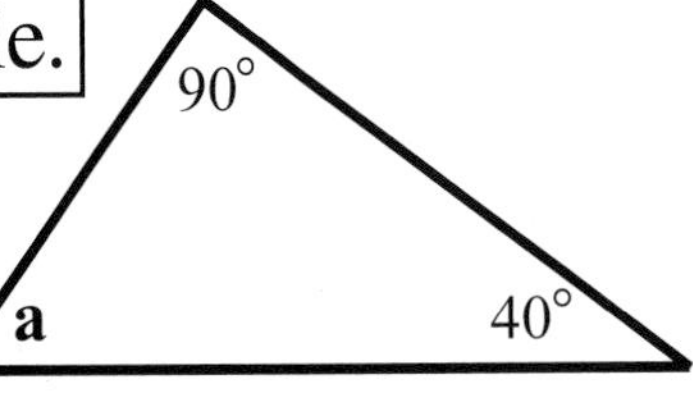

Missing **Angle a** $= 180 - (90 + 40)$

a $= 180 - 130 =$ **50°**

Example 2: Find **Angle a** in this Triangle.

Find Angle **b** first 180 − 125 = 55°

Missing **Angle a** = 180 − (50 + 55)

a = 180 − 105 = **75°**

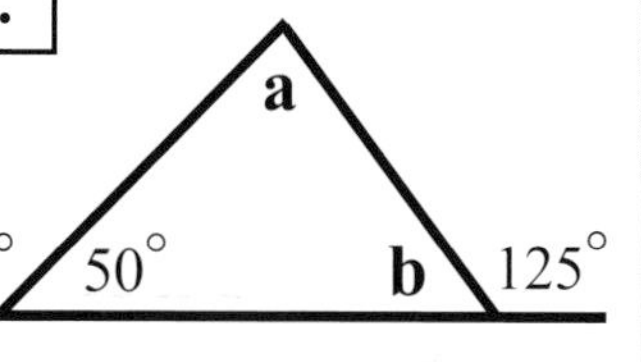

Example 3: Find **Angle a** in an Isosceles Triangle.

Angle **b** will also be 70°

Missing **Angle a** = 180 − (70 + 70)

a = 180 − 140 = **40°**

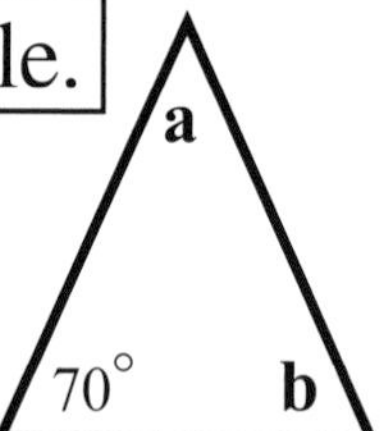

Exercise 15: 3a Answer the following:

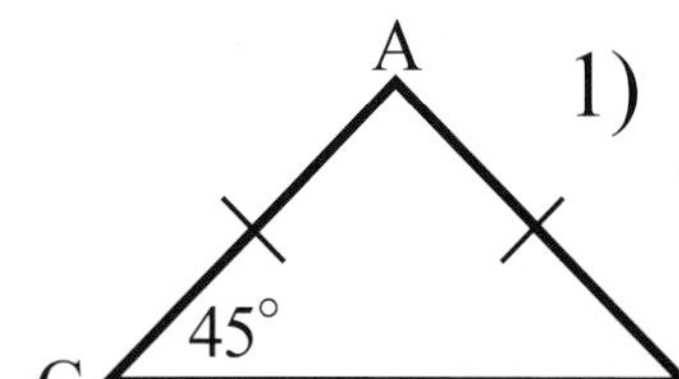

1) a) What Size is Angle $C\hat{A}B$? .... degrees.
   b) What Size is Angle $A\hat{B}C$? .... degrees.

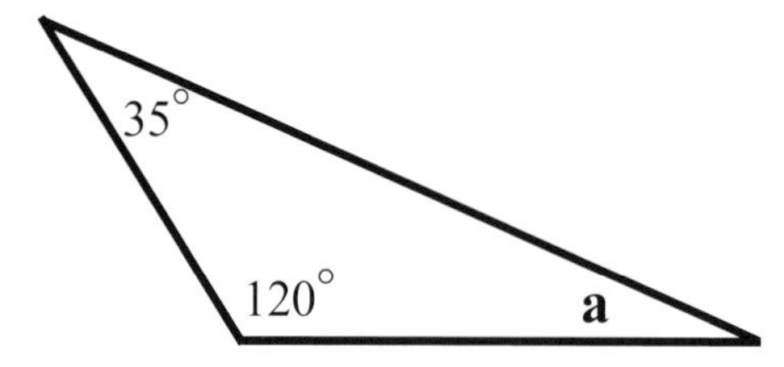

2) What is the Size of Angle **a**?
   It is .... degrees.

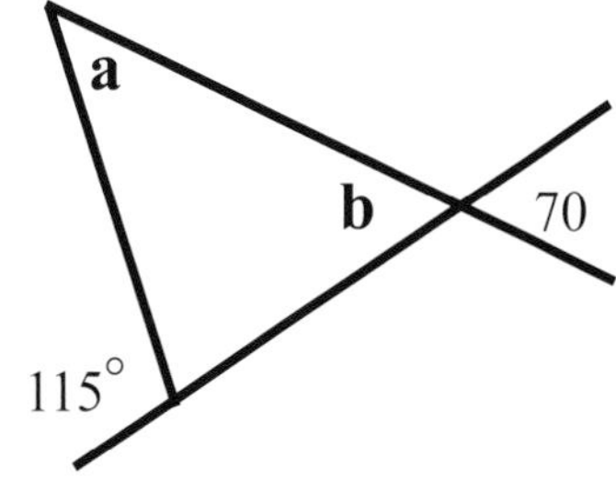

3) What Size are Angles a and b?
   a) Angle a is .... degrees.
   b) Angle b is .... degrees.

c. Quadrilaterals

The Interior Angles of a Quadrilateral add up to 360°.

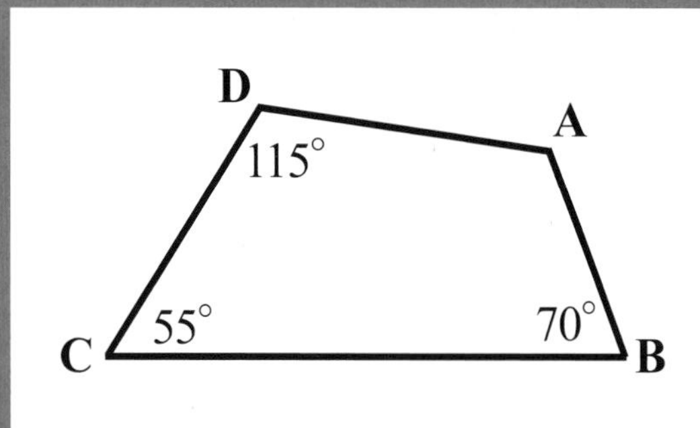

Example: Find **Angle $D\hat{A}B$.**

Add all the other Angles.

115 + 55 + 70 = 240°

Subtract from 360.

360 − 240 = **120°**

Exercise 15: 3b Answer the following:

125°
75° B
A

4) a) Angle $\hat{A}$ will be .... °
   b) Angle $\hat{B}$ will be .... °

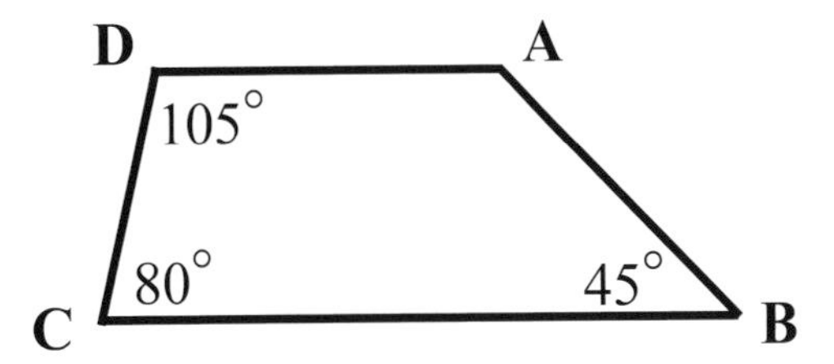

5) What is the Size of Angle $D\hat{A}B$? .... °

d. Polygona (Polygons)

Exterior/Interior Angles

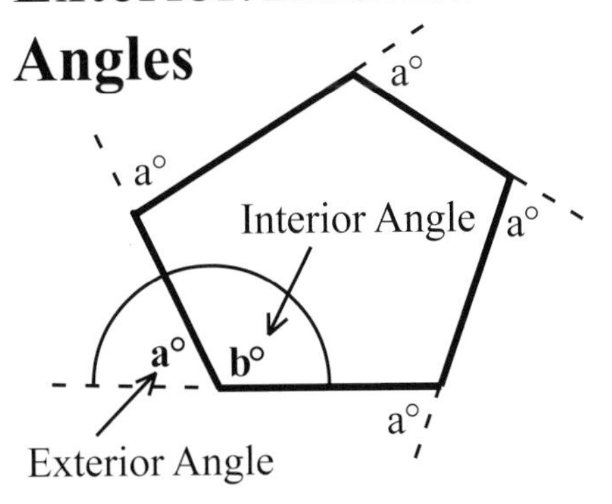

- Interior + Exterior Angle (a + b) of **all** Polygons = **180°**.
- The **Sum** (total) of the **Exterior Angles** (5 × Angle a) = **360°** This applies to **all** Polygons.

Find the Sum of the Interior Angles in this Pentagon.
Multiply the Interior/Exterior Angles by the number of Sides.
$5 \times 180 = 900$
Subtract the Sum of the Exterior Angles (360) from this total (900).
$900 - 360 = 540$
The Interior Angles of this Pentagon add up to 540°.

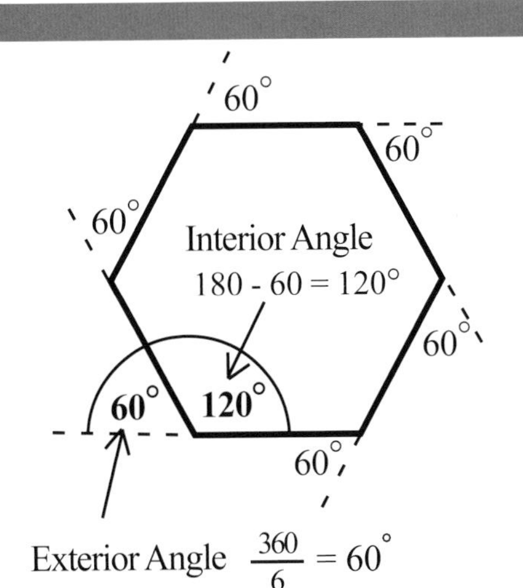

Finding an Exterior and Interior Angle in a Regular Polygon.
Divide the Sum of the Exterior Angles by the number of Sides.
Exterior Angle = $360 \div 6 = 60°$
Subtract the Exterior Angle (60°) from the Interior + Exterior Angle.
Interior Angle = $180 - 60 = 120°$

The Exterior Angle = 60°. The Interior Angle = 120°.

Exercise 15: 3c Answer the following:

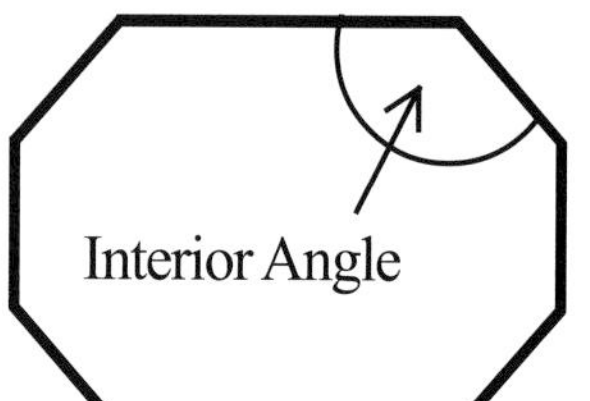

6) What is the **Sum (total) of all the Interior Angles** in this Irregular Octagon?

(Multiply) $8 \times 180 =$ ....°

(Subtract) .... $- 360 =$ ....°

The **Sum of all the Interior Angles** would be ....°

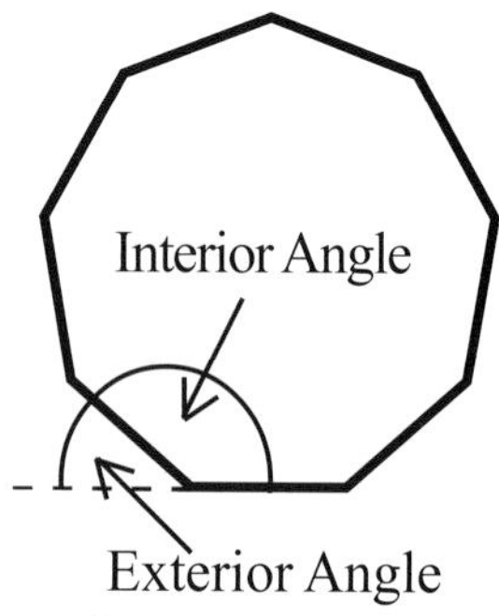

7) What is the Size of each **Interior and Exterior Angle** in this Regular Nonagon?

Exterior Angle (Divide) $\frac{360}{9}$ ....°

Interior Angle (Subract) $180 -$ .... = ...°

The **Sum of all the Interior Angles** would be ....°

Angle properties of Regular (Equal Sided) Polygons are based on Triangles.

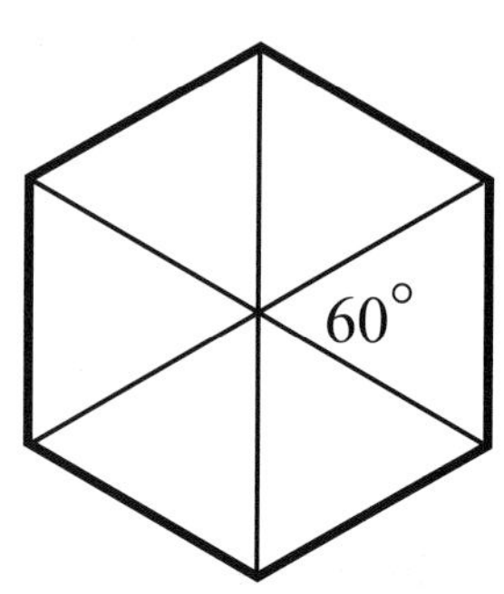

There are 360° in one Complete Turn of a Circle. The **Angles around the Centre of the Hexagon** Add up to 360°. Therefore each Angle must be **60°**. Hexagons are made up of **Equilateral Triangles** so the other Angles are all **60°**.

Example: Find **Angle b** in this Regular Pentagon.

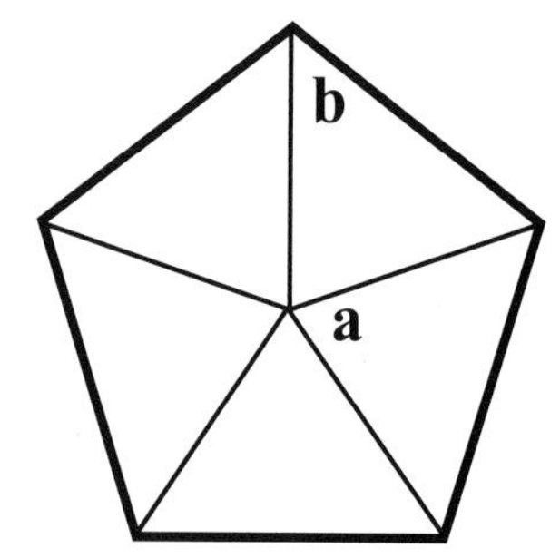

Find Angle a first
$360 \div 5 = 72°$

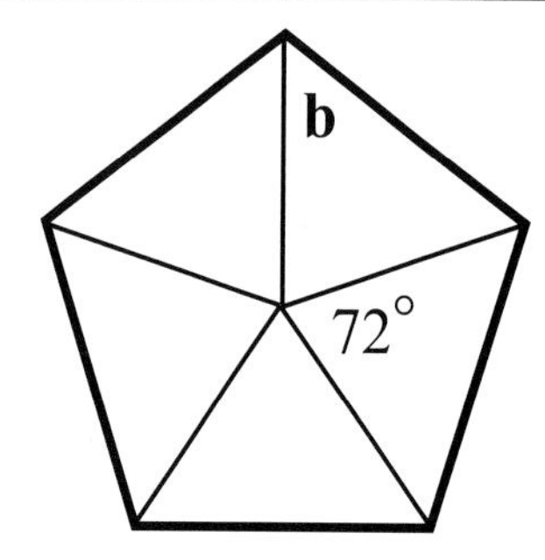

Angle **a** is 72°

All the Angles of a Triangle Add up to 180°.
$180 - 72 = 108$
Isosceles Triangles have 2 Equal Angles.
$108 \div 2 = 54$
Angle b is 54°.

Exercise 15: 3d Answer the following: **Score**

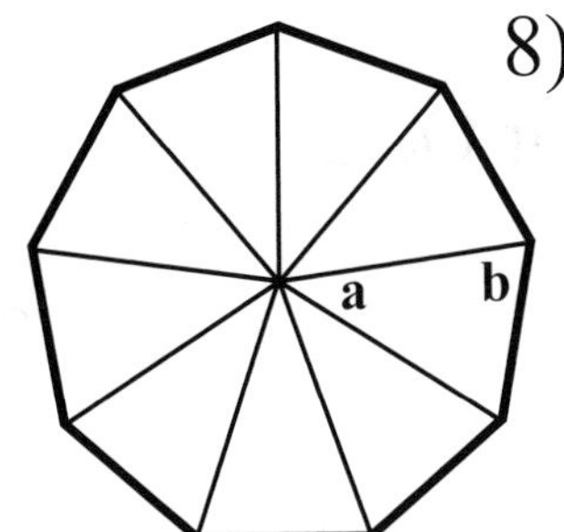

8) What is the Size of Angle **a** and **b** in this Regular Nonagon?

Angle a **(Divide)** $\frac{360}{9}$ = ...$^{\circ}$

Angle b **(Subtract)** 180 − .... = ...$^{\circ}$

(Divide) $\frac{?}{2}$ = ...$^{\circ}$

9) The Size of **Angle a** is ....$^{\circ}$

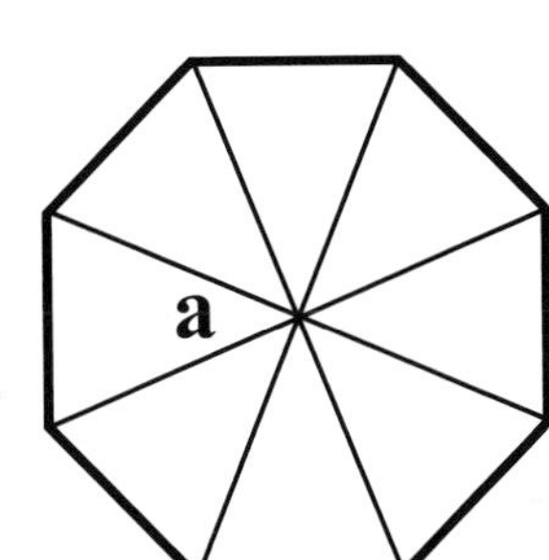

10) If the Angles in these Shapes were put in Size order the one in the middle would be ....

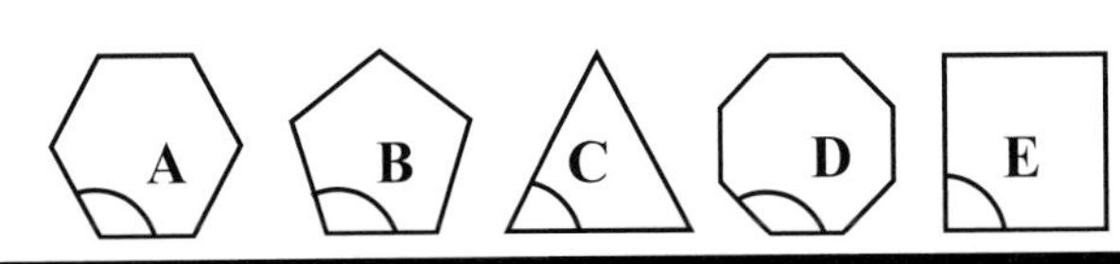

3. Three Dimensional Shapes

a. Polyhedra (Polyhedrons)

To help with learning three dimensional shapes, think about:

Edges **Vertices** **Faces**

A **Polyhedron** is a **Solid Shape** with 'Many Faces'. If each Face is exactly the same Size and Shape it is **Regular**.

Hexahedrons

A Cube

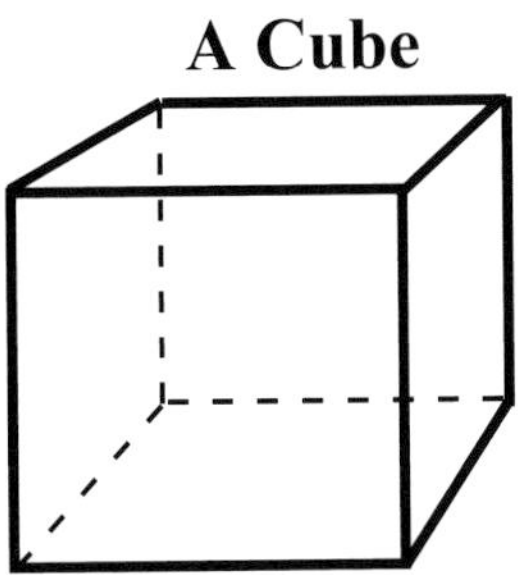

- 6 Equal Faces (Sides).
- 12 Equal Edges.
- 8 Vertices (Corners).

A Cuboid

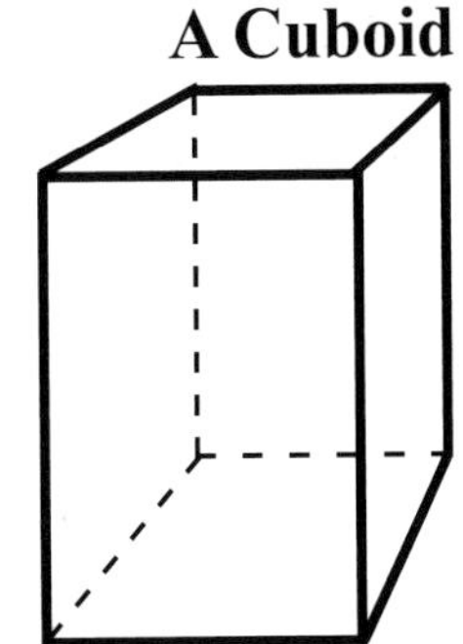

- 6 Faces (Sides).
- 12 Edges.
- 8 Vertices (Corners).

Octahedron

- Regular Octahedrons are made from Equilateral Triangles.
- 8 Faces (Sides).
- 12 Edges.
- 6 Vertices (Corners).

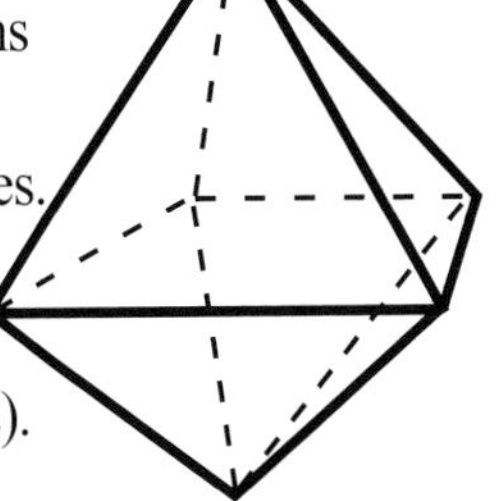

Square Pyramid

- 5 Faces (Sides).
- 8 Edges.
- 5 Vertices (Corners).

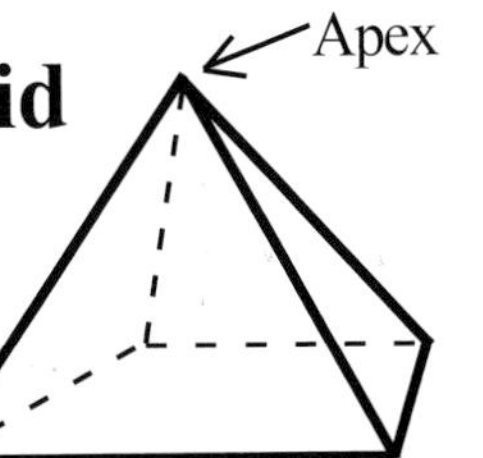

Triangular Pyramid (Tetrahedron)

- Regular Tetrahedrons are made from Equilateral Triangles.
- 4 Faces.
- 6 Edges.
- 4 Vertices (Corners).

Dodecahedron

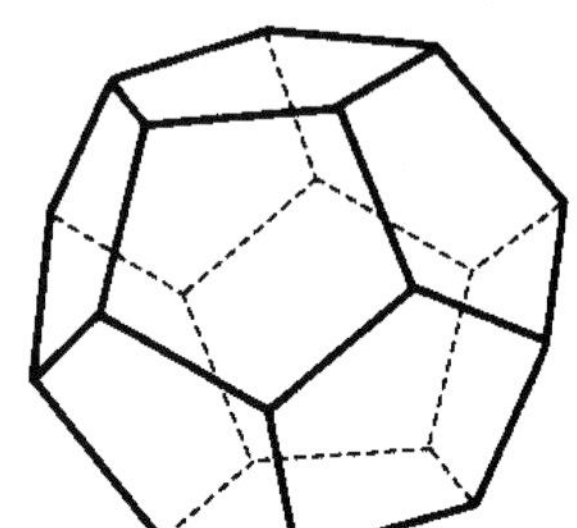

- 12 Faces (Sides).
- Each Face is a Regular Pentagon.

Icosahedron

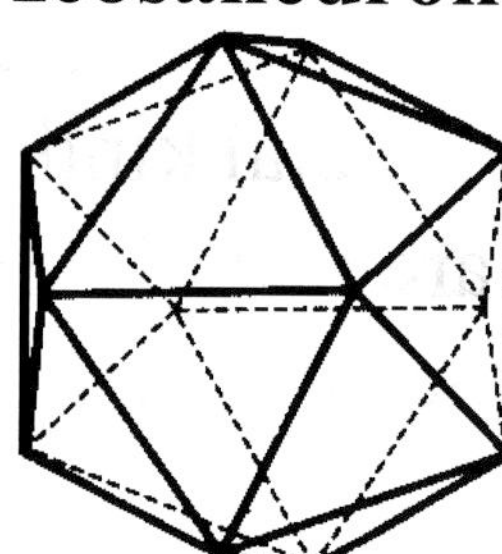

- 20 Faces (Sides).
- Each Face is an Equilateral Triangle.

Other Irregular Polyhedrons

Pentahedron (5 Faces).
Heptahedron (7 Faces).

Deltahedrons (plural **is Deltahedra**) are Polyhedra with Equilateral Triangles as their Faces. Tetrahedrons, Octahedrons and Icosahedrons can be Deltahedrons.

Euler's Theorem for Solids: Faces + Corners = Edges + 2

Example: Demonstrate Euler's Theorem with a Cube.

A Cube has: **6** Faces + **8** Corners = **12** Edges + **2**

14 = **14**

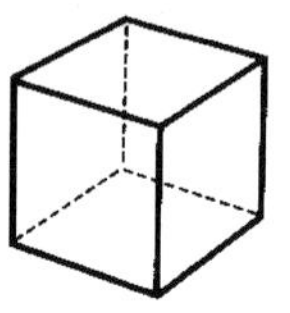

Exercise 15: 4a Answer the following:

1) What two Shapes have the same number of Edges, Faces and Vertices? .... and ....

2) Which two Shapes have the same number of Edges?

A 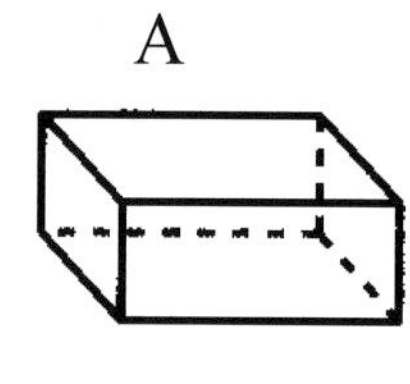
B 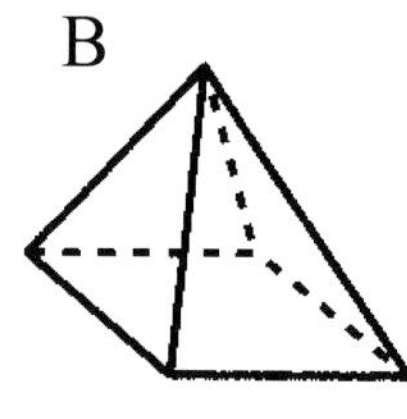
C 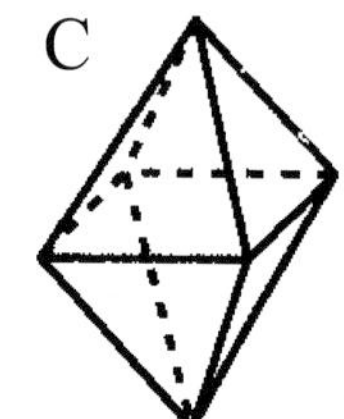
D 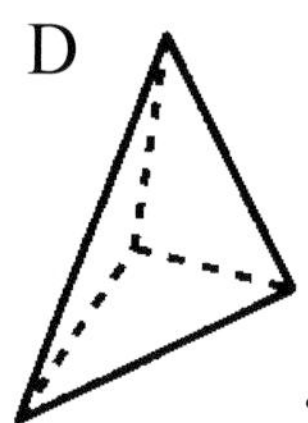

.... and ....

3) Shapes with a) 8 Faces are called ....
b) 12 Faces are called ....
c) 20 Faces are called ....

4) Two Shapes have the same number of Faces as Vertices. They are a .... and a
....

5) Which Shape has more Faces than Vertices?

A 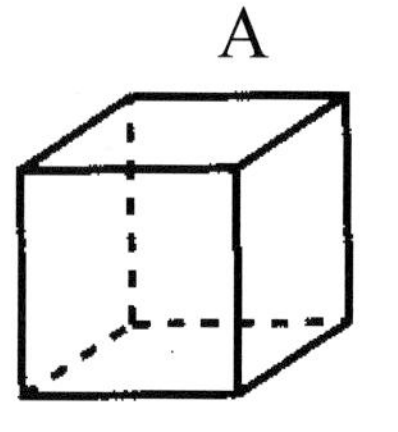
B 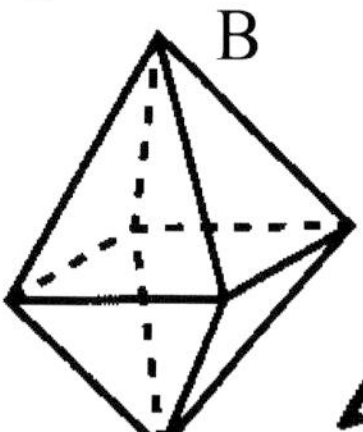
C 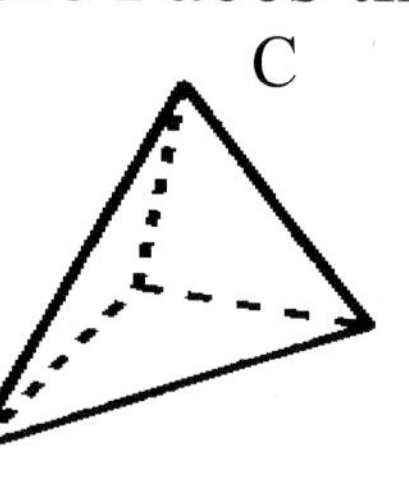
D 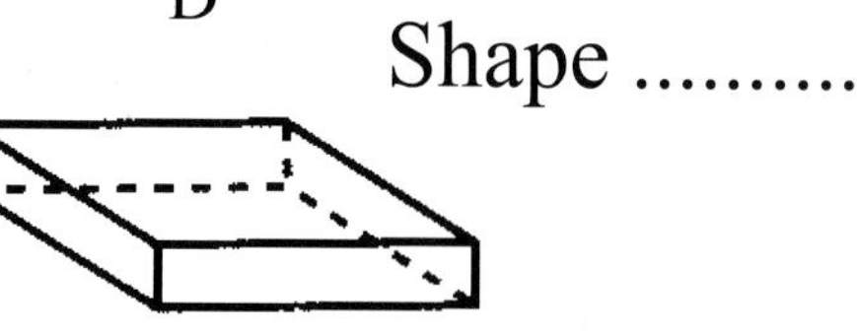

Shape ....

b. Prisms

A Prism is a special kind of Solid Shape.

- Both ends are exactly the same Size and Shape.
- Both ends are Parallel to each other.

Examples:

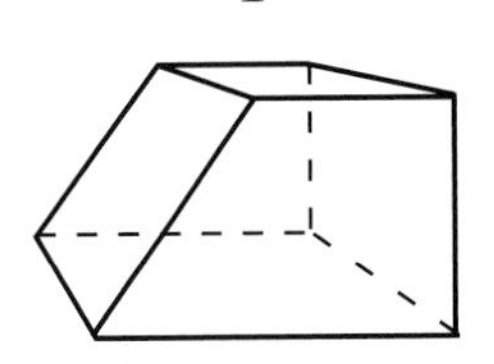

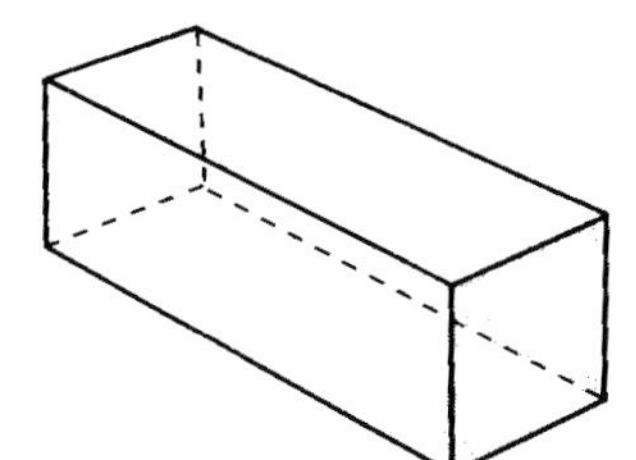

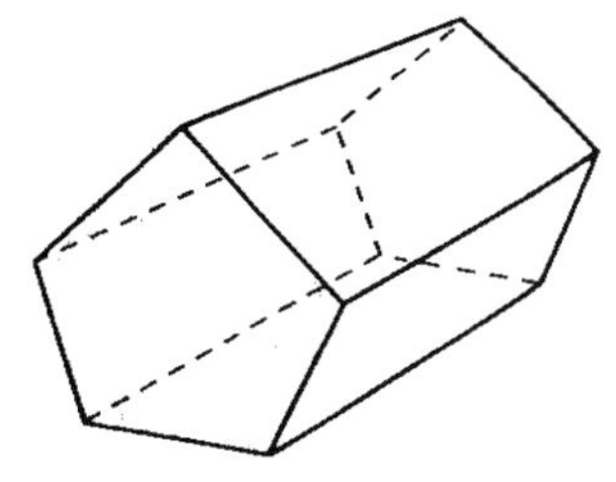

Triangular Prism

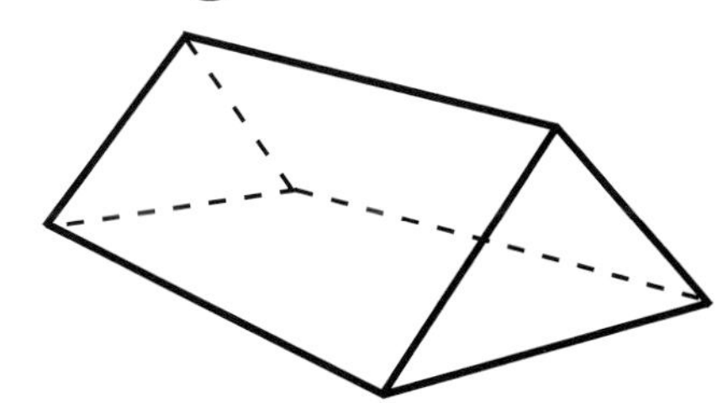

Hexagonal Prism

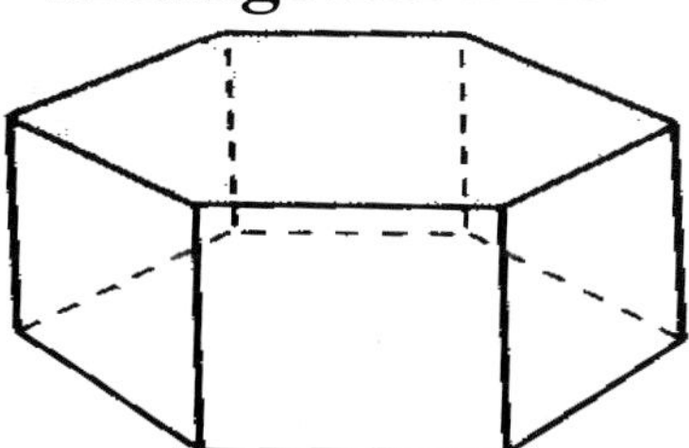

Exercise 15: 4b Answer the following:

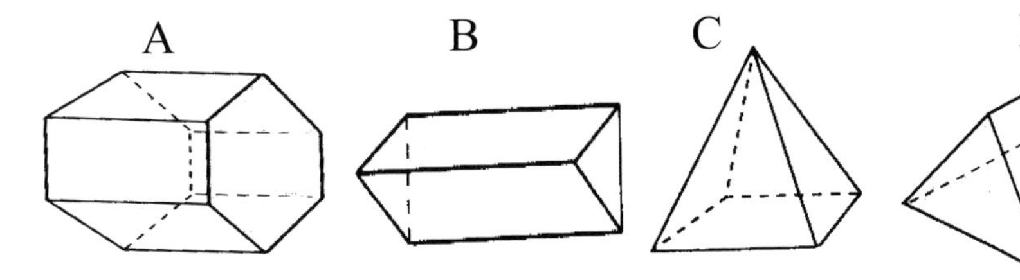

E

6) List the shapes that are Prisms. ....

7) A Triangular Prism has ...... Faces ...... Edges ...... Vertices.

c. Circular Shapes

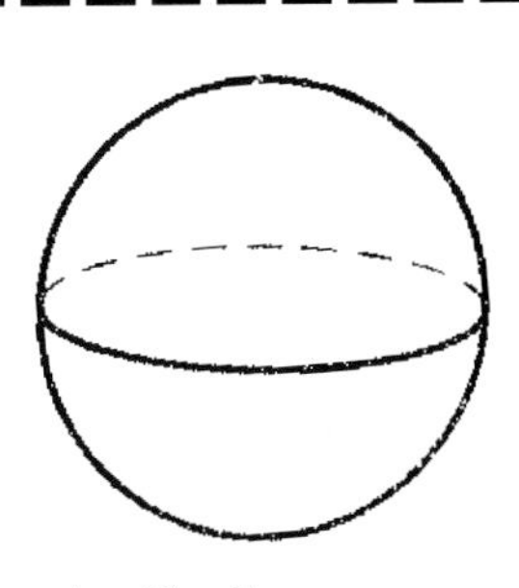

A Sphere
(A ball)

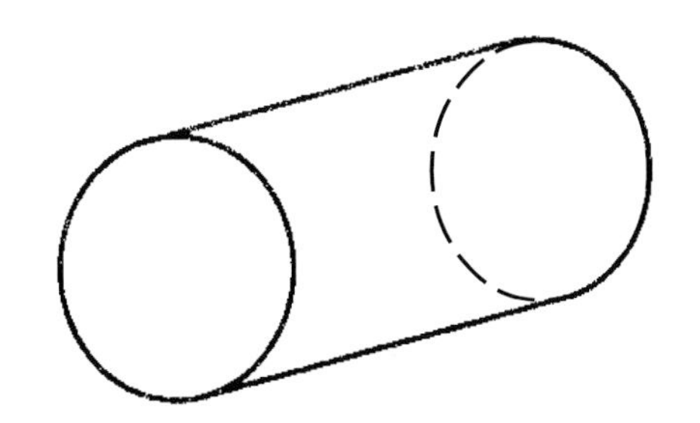

A Cylinder
(A Roller Shape)

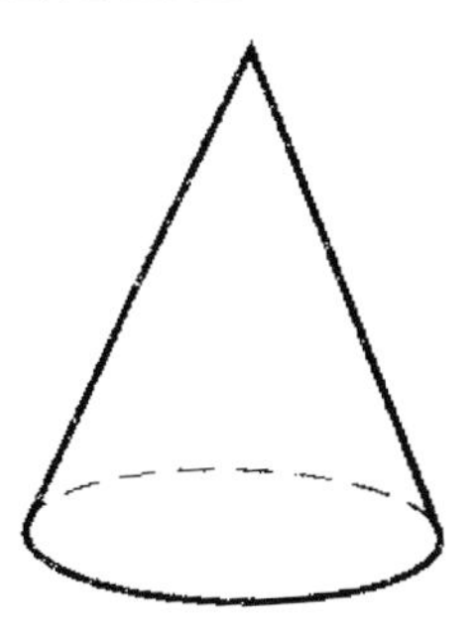

A Cone

Exercise 15: 4c Answer the following:

8) Which Circular Shape is pointed at one end? ....

9) Which of these Shapes is round with no Edges? ....

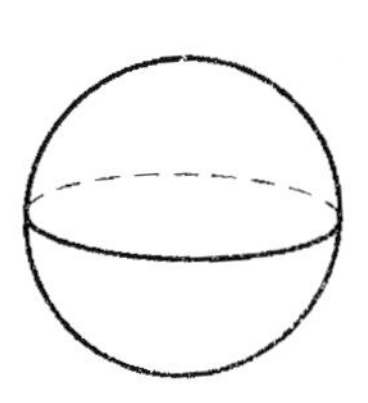
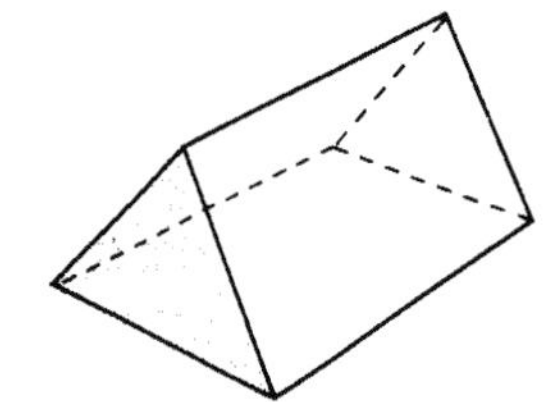
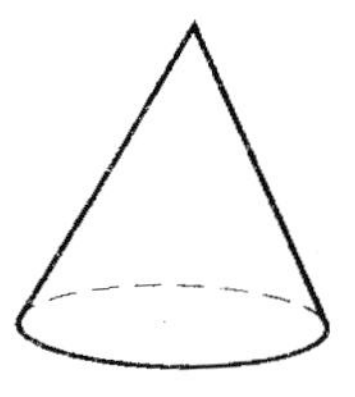
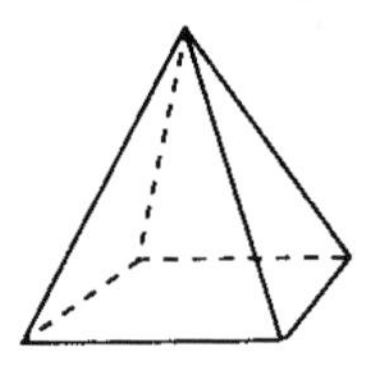

10) What Circular Shape has flat Circles at each end which are Parallel to each other? ....

Score

4. Representing Solids

a. Nets

A Net is a pattern. It is a flat Shape which can be cut out and folded up to make a Solid Shape.

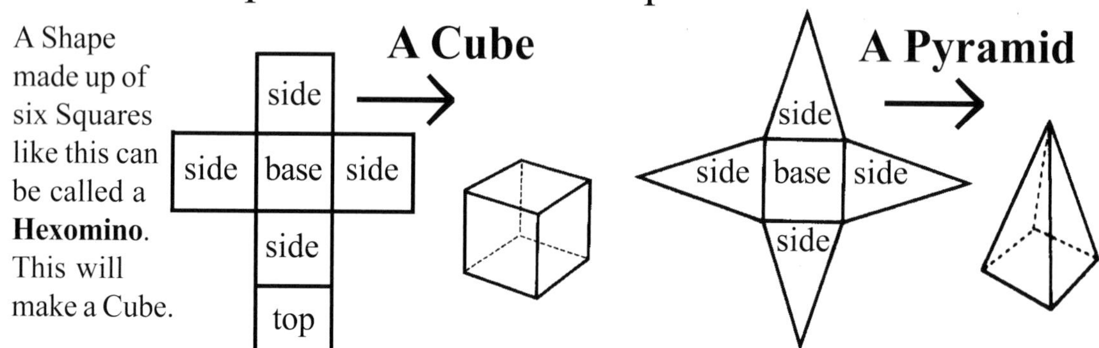

Exercise 15: 5a Answer the following:

1) Which Net will make the Triangular Prism?

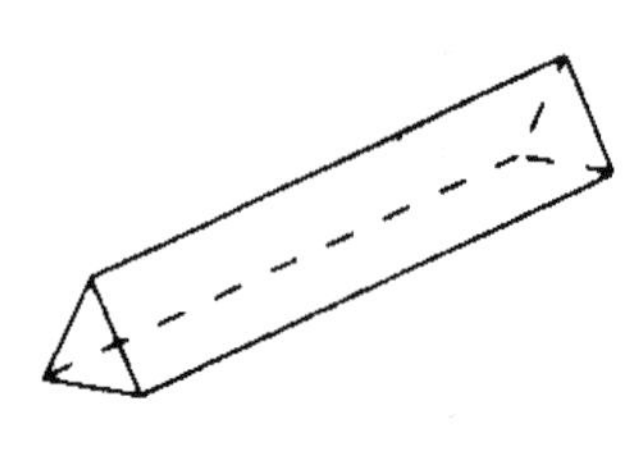

A 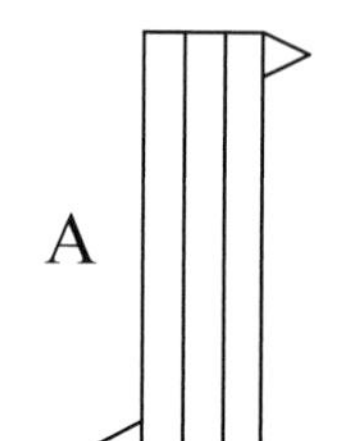

B 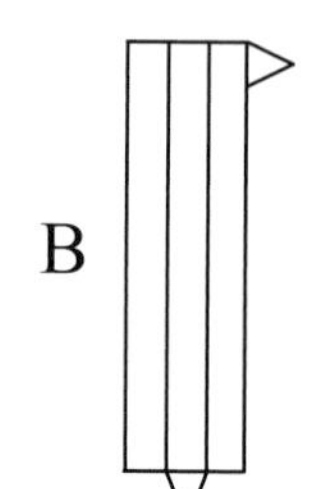

C 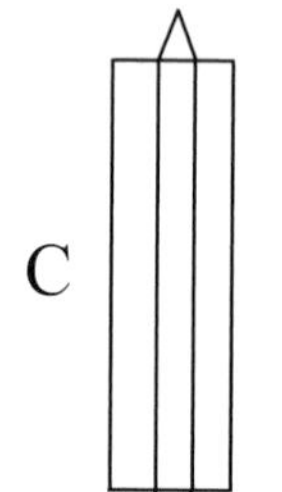

2) What Solid Shape will this Net make?

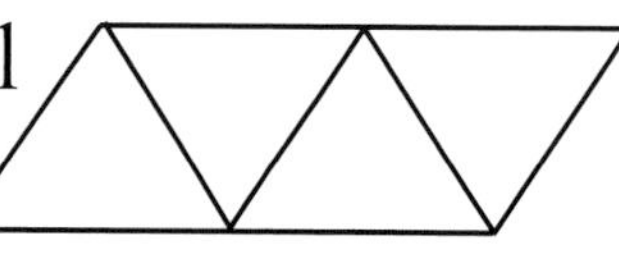

....

....

3) This Net will make a: ....

4) This is a Net for a: ....

5) This will make a: ....

6) Which Net will make the Regular Tetrahedron?

A B C D ....

b. Planes of Symmetry

3-D Shapes have no Lines of Symmetry, but have **Planes of Symmetry**. It is the 3-D Equivalent of a Line of Symmetry.

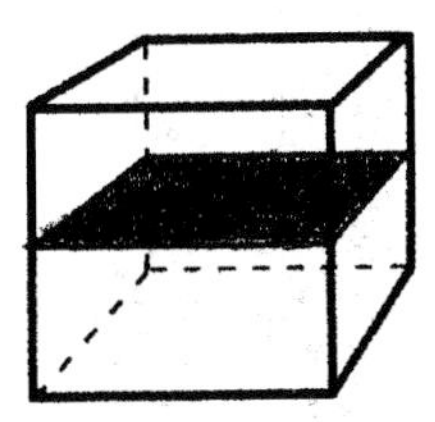

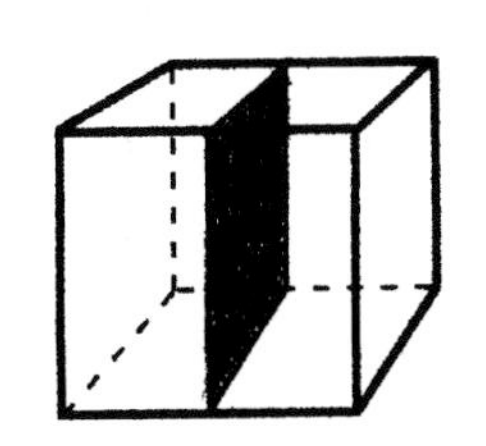

A Cube has a number of Planes of Symmetry. Only two are shown.

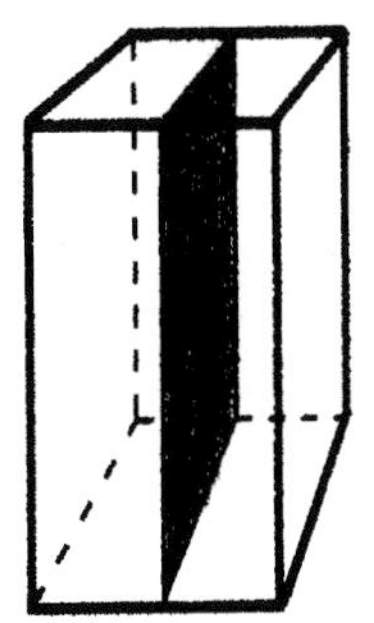

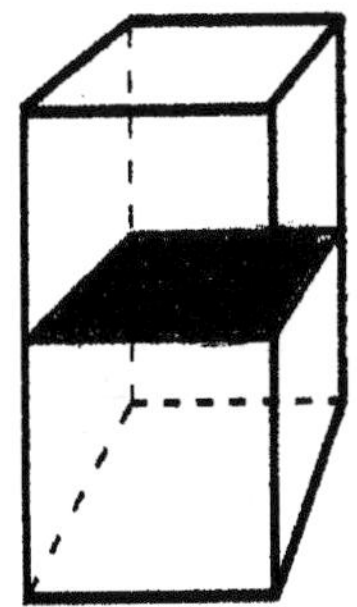

A Cuboid can have five Planes of Symmetry. 2 have been shown above.

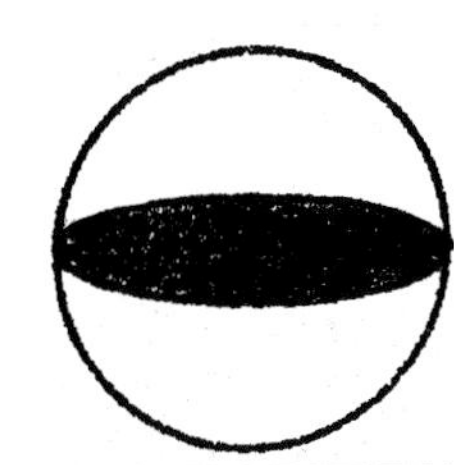

A Sphere has an infinite (endless) number of Planes of Symmetry. Only one is shown.

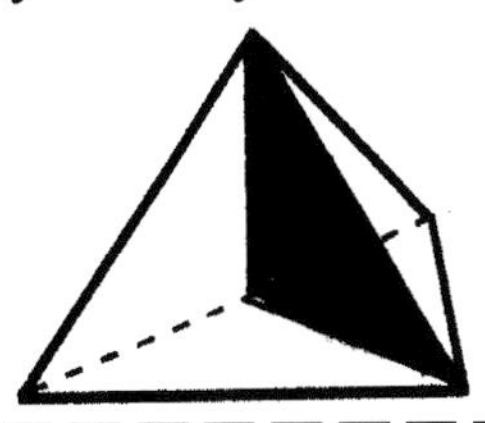

One Plane of Symmetry is shown on this Tetrahedron.

Exercise 15: 5b Answer the following:

7) How many Planes of Symmetry does this Triangular Prism have?

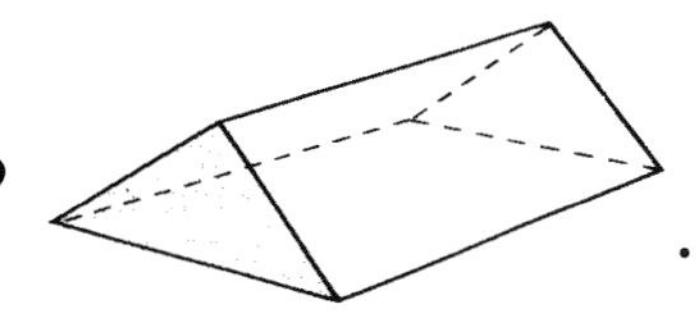

....

8) How many Planes of Symmetry does this Cone have? ....

c. Isometric Projections

Isometric Drawings show 3-D shapes from three view-points (Elevations). They form the basis for Isometric Projections.

Example: A Triangular Prism drawn Isometrically.

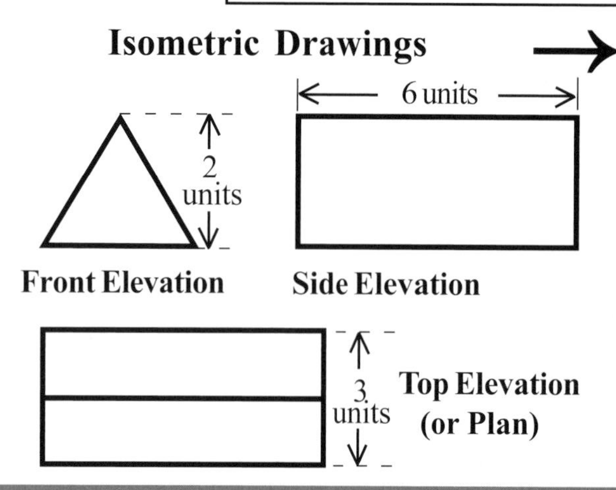

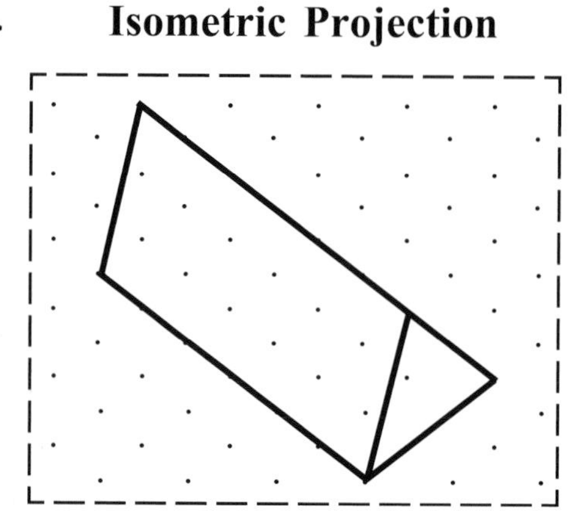

Exercise 15: 5c

9) Draw this Shape as an Isometric Projection:

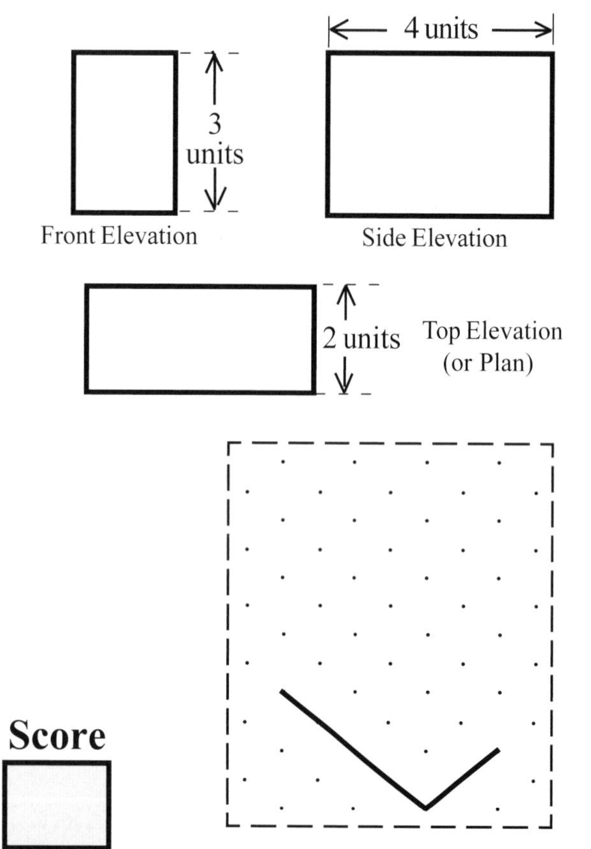

10) Complete the drawings for this Projection:

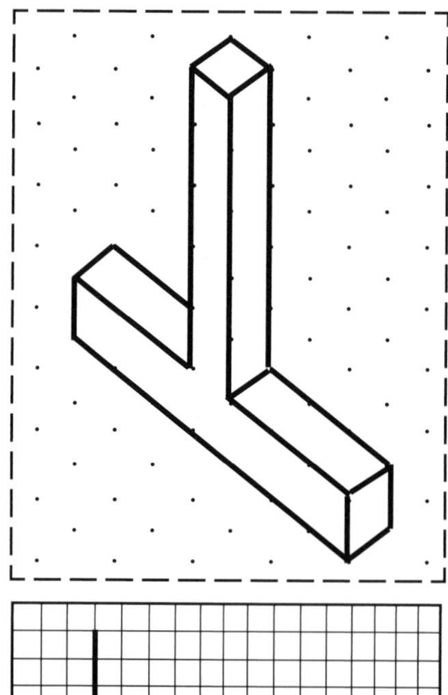

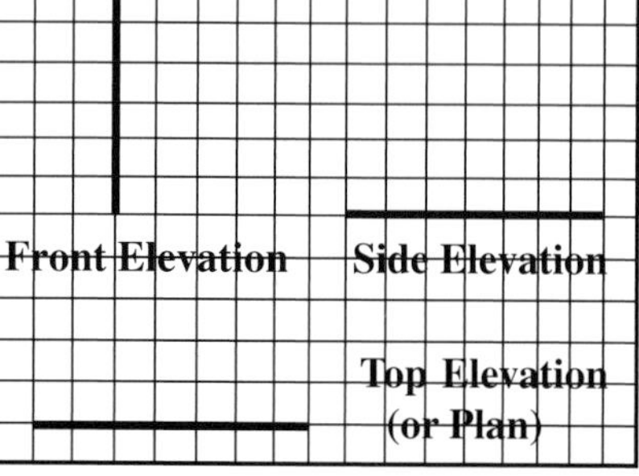

Score

Answers

Probability

Exercise 11: 1

1) Unlikely 2) Certain
3) Likely 4) Possible
5) Likely 6) Unlikely
7) Impossible 8) Certain
9) Unlikely 10) Likely

Exercise 11: 2a

1) a) No b) Yes
2) a) Yes b) No
3) a) Unfair b) Fair
4) Fair 5) Unfair

Exercise 11: 2b

6) Yes 7) Yes
8) Yes 9) No
10) a) Yes b) No

Exercise 11: 3a

1) Heads or Tails
2) 1, 2, 3, 4 ,5, 6
3) green, red, blue, yellow
4) Hearts, diamonds, spades, clubs

Exercise 11: 3b

5) GG, GW, GB, WG WW, WB, BG, BW BB
6) AB, AC, AD, BC BD, CD

Exercise 11: 3c

7)

Spinner 1	Spinner 2
A	D
A	E
A	F
B	D
B	E
B	F
C	D
C	E
C	F

8)

Name 1	Name 2
P	R
P	S
P	T
R	S
R	T
S	T

Exercise 11: 3d

9a) H1, H2, H3, H4, H5, H6, T1, T2 T3, T4, T5, T6

9b)

	1	2	3	4	5	6
8	9	10	11	12	13	14
7	8	9	10	11	12	13
6	7	8	9	10	11	12
5	6	7	8	9	10	11
4	5	6	7	8	9	10
3	4	5	6	7	8	9
2	3	4	5	6	7	8
1	2	3	4	5	6	7

Exercise 11: 3e

10a) 80% 0.8 $\frac{4}{5}$

10b) 12 children

Exercise 11: 4a

1) $\frac{1}{10}$ or 1 in 10
2) $\frac{3}{20}$ or 3 in 20
3) $\frac{1}{4}$ or 1 in 4

Exercise 11: 4b

4) a) $\frac{1}{6}$ or 1 in 6
b) $\frac{1}{3}$ or 1 in 3
c) $\frac{1}{2}$ or 1 in 2
d) Blue
5) a) $\frac{11}{25}$ or 11 in 25
b) $\frac{6}{25}$ or 6 in 25
6) a) 60% b) 40%
c) 0.2 d) 0.8
7) a) $\frac{1}{13}$ or 1 in 13
b) $\frac{1}{2}$ or 1 in 2
c) $\frac{3}{13}$ or 3 in 13

Exercise 11: 4c

8a) $\frac{4}{9}$ or 4 in 9
b) $\frac{3}{4}$ or 3 in 4
c) $\frac{13}{21}$ or 13 in 21

Exercise 11: 4d

9a) 0.16 b) 0.2

Exercise 11: 4e

10a) 18 tests
b) 120 times

Exercise 11: 5a

1) $\frac{1}{7}$ or 1 in 7
2) $\frac{1}{7}$ or 1 in 7
3) $\frac{1}{2}$ or 1 in 2
4) $\frac{1}{16}$ or 1 in 16
5) $\frac{1}{8}$ or 1 in 8
6) $\frac{1}{4}$ or 1 in 4
7) $\frac{3}{4}$ or 3 in 4
8a) $\frac{1}{2}$ or 1 in 2
b) $\frac{1}{12}$ or 1 in 12
c) $\frac{1}{4}$ or 1 in 4

Exercise 11: 5b

9a) 0.42 b) 0.49

Exercise 11: 5c

10a) $\frac{3}{7}$ b) $\frac{7}{15}$

Answers

Chapter Twelve
Lines and Angles

Exercise 12: 1a

1) Parallel
2) Perpendicular
3) 8 horizontal sides
4) Parallel
5) 3 vertical sides

Exercise 12: 1b

6) d and h 7) c and e
8) b, f and g 9) Obtuse
10) Reflex

Exercise 12: 2

1) 60° - supplementary
2) 33° - complementary
3) 100° - conjugate
4) 75° - opposite
5) 120° - conjugate
6) 60° - supplementary
7) 55° - adjacent
8) 50° - interior/allied
9) 130° - corresponding
10) Obtuse, Acute, Reflex

Exercise 12: 3a

1) $\frac{2}{5}$ 2) $\frac{7}{10}$ 3) $\frac{1}{6}$

4) $\frac{7}{12}$ 5) $\frac{1}{15}$

Exercise 12: 3b

6) 135° 7) 150°
8) 80° 9) 240°
10) 300°

Exercise 12: 4

1) South-east 2) 045°
3) South 4) West
5) 135° 6) 225°
7) 90° 8) South
9) 180° 10) South-west

Exercise 12: 5

1) 315° 2) 070°
3a) 300° 3b) 260°
3c) 335° 3d) 230°
4) 160° 5) 340°
6) 315° 7) 135°
8) 270° 9) 090°
10) 310°

Chapter Thirteen
Time

Exercise 13: 1a

1) 10 decades
2) 2,000 years
3) Yes, 2016 is a leap yr
4) 21st century
5) 38 months
6) 7 months
7) The year 2022

Exercise 13: 1b

8) 74 days
9) 92 days
10) 9 days

Exercise 13: 2

1) 14. 04. 75
2) 20. 08. 55
3) 01. 02. 20
4) 11. 05. 63
5) 22. 12. 97
6) 10th November 1954
7) 3rd July 1989
8) 17th March 1974
9) 14th September 1996
10) 22nd October 1945

Exercise 13: 3

1) 12. 03. 99
2) 07. 01. 82
3) 11. 07. 97
4) 24. 11. 74
5) 23. 03. 86
6) 25. 10. 00
7) 10. 09. 58
8) 21. 05. 67
9) Thursday
10) Monday

Exercise 13: 4

1) 90 minutes
2) 240 minutes
3) 195 minutes
4) 1 hour 17 minutes
5) 1 hour 31 minutes
6) 3 hours 32 minutes
7) 150 seconds
8) 300 seconds
9) 1 minute 29 seconds
10) 3 minutes 20 seconds

Exercise 13: 5

1) $\frac{1}{5}$ hour 2) $\frac{1}{6}$ hour

3) $\frac{3}{5}$ hour 4) $\frac{5}{12}$ hour

5) $\frac{1}{15}$ hour 6) 50 minutes
7) 42 minutes
8) 48 minutes
9) 55 minutes
10) 18 minutes

Exercise 13: 6

1) 18° 2) 60° 3) 336°
4) 72° 5) 144°
6) 6 minutes
7) 55 minutes
8) 41 minutes
9) 17 minutes
10) 39 minutes

Exercise 13: 7

1) 3 minutes to 7 a.m.
 6.57 a.m.
2) Quarter past 7 p.m.
 7.15 p.m.
3) 26 minutes past 2 p.m.
 2.26 p.m.

Answers

4) 12 minutes to 11 a.m.
   10.48 a.m.
5) 4 minutes past 5 p.m.
   5.04 p.m.
6) 3 minutes past 4 a.m.
   4.03 a.m.
7) 6 minutes to 9 a.m.
   8.54 a.m.
8) 7 minutes past 6 p.m.
   6.07 p.m.
9) 57 minutes
10) 34 minutes

Exercise 13: 8
1) 1806 hours 2) 1026 hours
3) 1112 hours 4) 1952 hours
5) 1544 hours 6) 2326 hours
7) 0313 hours 8) 1848
9) 1118, 1131, 1144
10) 0613, 0623, 0633,
    0643, 0653

Exercise 13: 9
1) 0845 2) 2230
3) 0000 4) 0936
5) 3 minutes to 12 a.m.
   or 3 minutes to midnight
   11.57 p.m.
6) 27 minutes to 4 a.m.
   3.33 a.m.
7) 19 minutes past 5 p.m.
   5.19 p.m.
8) 12 o'clock noon
   12.00 noon or 12 p.m.
9) Quarter past 9 a.m.
   9.15 a.m.
10) 14 minutes to 9 a.m.
    8.46 a.m.

Exercise 13: 10a
1) 9.55 p.m.
2) 0202 hours
3) 4.48 p.m, 4.24 p.m.
   4.03 p.m.
4) 1 hour 14 minutes
5) 11 hours 10 minutes

Exercise 13: 10b
6) 9 hours 40 minutes
7) 14 hours 27 minutes
8) Train D
   2 hours 49 minutes
9) 14 hours 41 minutes
10) 1 hour 46 minutes

Exercise 13: 11a
1) 9 hours 55 minutes
2) 4 days 12 hours
   0 minutes
3) 1 hour 38 minutes
   0 seconds
4) 5 hours 15 minutes
5) 5 hours 50 minutes

Exercise 13: 11b
6) 1 hour 55 minutes
7) 50 minutes
8) 1 hour 30 minutes
9) 20 minutes
10) 7 hours 30 minutes

Exercise 13: 12a
1a) 2yrs 11mths
 b) 11yrs 3mths
 c) 3yrs 4mths

Exercise 13: 12b
2) 2hrs 27mins

Exercise 13: 12c
3) 11.59 a.m. 4) 9.06 a.m.
5) 7.28 a.m. 6) 7.30 p.m.
7) 10.01 a.m.

Exercise 13: 12d
8) Train D - fastest
   Train B - slowest
9a) Train A
9b) Train A is the fastest
10a) Train C
10b) 2 minutes difference

Exercise 13: 13
1) 04:00 2) 12:00
3) 05:00 4) 13:30
5) 6.00 p.m. 6) 5.30 a.m.
7) 6.00 p.m. 8) 4.00 p.m.
9) midnight 10) 10.00 a.m.

Exercise 13: 14
1) 3 days, 7 hours
   and 45 minutes
2) 4.21 p.m.
3) 43 hours 0 minutes
4) 19:02 hours
5) 1 hour 49 minutes
6) B - 1 hour 43 minutes
   C - 1 hour 13 minutes
7) Coach B
8) $\frac{5}{12}$ of the day
9) 35 minutes each
10) 57 hours 34 minutes

Exercise 13: 15a
1) 80km/h 2) 4mph

Exercise 13: 15b
3) 3mph 4) 720km/h

Exercise 13: 15c
5) 80 hours 6) 6 hours

Exercise 13: 15d
7) 15 minutes 8) 25 minutes

Exercise 13: 15e
9) 7 miles 10) 45km

Exercise 13: 16
1) 62mph 2) 24 minutes
3) 9km 4) 48km/h
5) 30km 6) 3 hours
7) 92 hours 8) 800mph
9) 4 hours 10) 4000 miles

Chapter Fourteen
Symmetry

Exercise 14: 1
1) B, C, D, E, H, I, K, O, X
2) A, H, I, M, O, T, U,
   V, W, X, Y
3) F, G, J, L, N, P, Q,
   R, S, Z

4) One 5) Three
6) Four
7) 8)

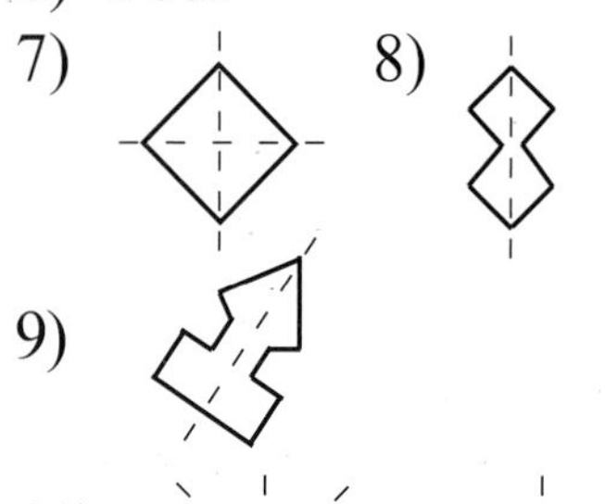

9)

10)

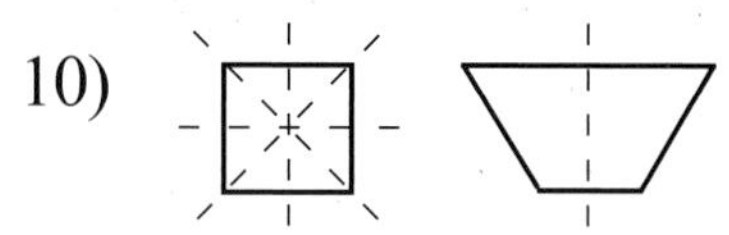

Exercise 14: 2
1) Order of 8
2) Order of 1
3) Order of 6
4) Order of 8
5) Order of 1
6) Order of 4
7) Order of 5
8) Order of 2
9) Order of 4
10) Shapes 2) and 5)

Chapter Fifteen
Shapes

Exercise 15: 1a
1) Isosceles, Scalene, Right Angle, Obtuse and Acute
2) a) Obtuse
   b) AB is a Median
3) a) Isosceles b) One
   c) One
4) a) Equilateral triangle
   b) 60 degrees
5) a) Scalene, Right Angle (Scalene)
   b) Order of 1

Exercise 15: 1b
6) In any order:
   a) Kite
   b) Isosceles Trapezium
   c) Arrowhead
7) Kite, Arrowhead
8) a)
   b) Rectangle
9) (General) Quadrilateral
10) a) Trapezium
   b) Parallelogram

Exercise 15: 2a
1) a) Irregular hexagon
   b) Irregular pentagon
   c) Regular dodecagon
2) 7 axes; 1 axis
   9 axes; 6 axes
3) Any three: Triangle, pentagon, heptagon nonagon, hendecagon, quindecagon
4) 3 shapes
5) Order of 1; 1; 8

Exercise 15: 2b
6) a) Diameter
   b) Radius
   c) Circumference
7) a) Order of 2
   b) 2
8) a) Semi-circle
   b) Order of 1
9) a) Sector
   b) Quadrant
10) a) Segment
   b) Chord

Exercise 15: 3a
1) a) 90 degrees
   b) 45 degrees
2) 25 degrees
3) a) 45 degrees
   b) 70 degrees

Exercise 15: 3b
4) a) 125° b) 35°
5) 130°

Exercise 15: 3c
6) Sum (interior) = 1080°
7) Exterior = 40°
   Interior = 140°
   Sum (interior) = 1260°

Exercise 15: 3d
8) Angle a = 40°
   Angle b = 70°
9) Angle a is 45°
10) Shape B

Exercise 15: 4a
1) Cubes and cuboids
2) A and C
3) a) Octahedrons
   b) Dodecahedrons
   c) Icosahedrons
4) Square pyramid and triangular pyramid (tetrahedron)
5) Shape B

Exercise 15: 4b
6) A, B and D
7) 5 faces, 9 edges and 6 vertices

Exercise 15: 4c
8) A cone 9) A sphere
10) A cylinder

Exercise 15: 5a
1) Net C
2) Triangular pyramid or tetrahedron
3) A cube 4) A cuboid
5) A square pyramid
6) Net B

Exercise 15: 5b
7) 2 planes
8) Endless (infinite)

Exercise 15: 5c
9)

10)

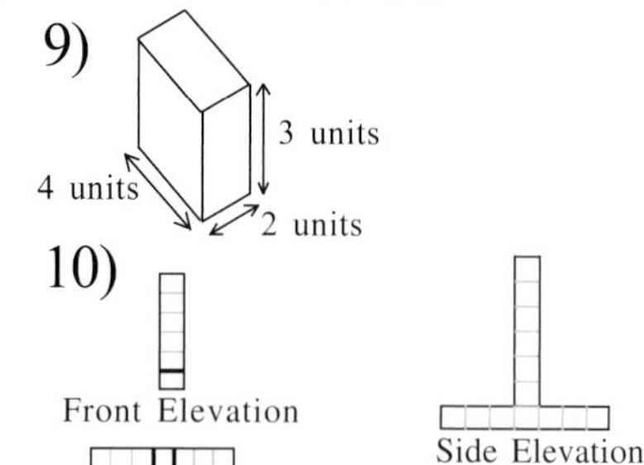

PROGRESS CHARTS

11. PROBABILITY

Scores: 10, 9, 8, 7, 6, 5, 4, 3, 2, 1

Exercises: 1, 2, 3, 4, 5

Total Score

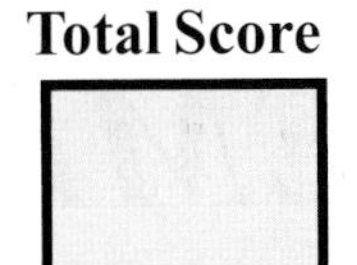

Percentage

%

12. LINES & ANGLES

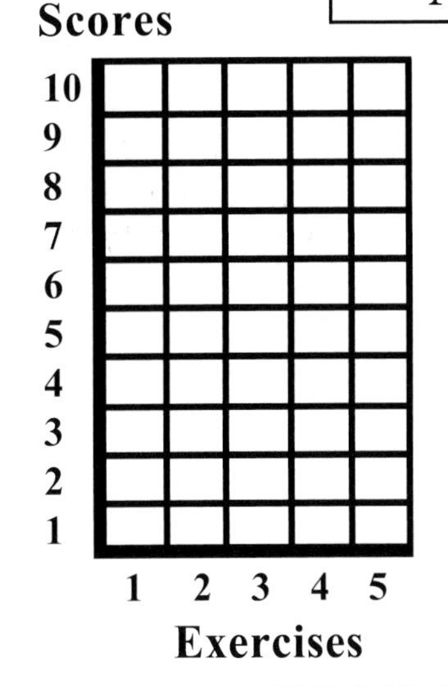

Total Score

Percentage

%

13. TIME

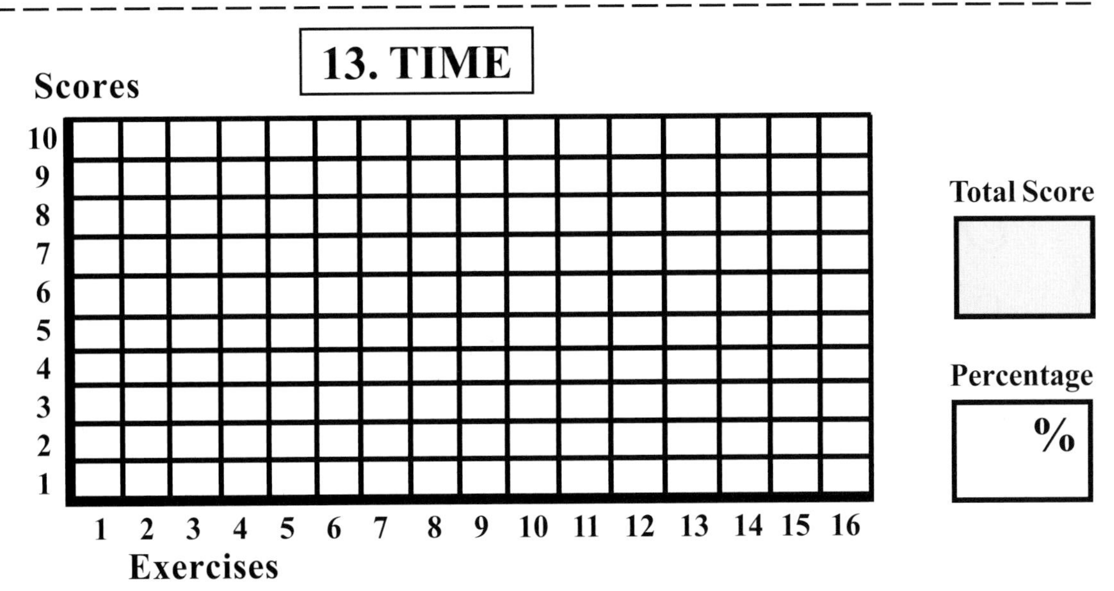

Total Score

Percentage

%

14. SYMMETRY

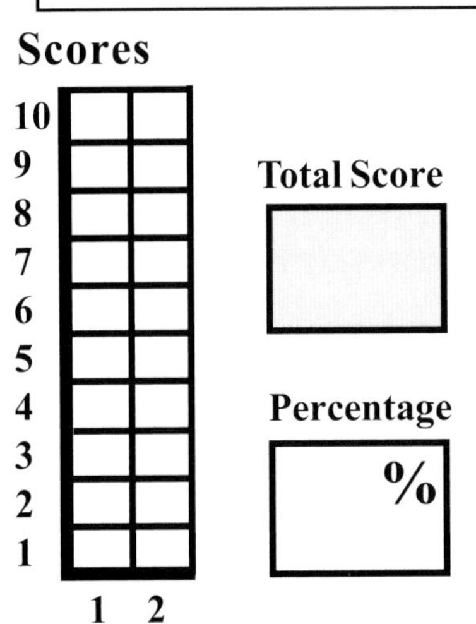

Total Score

Percentage

%

15. SHAPES

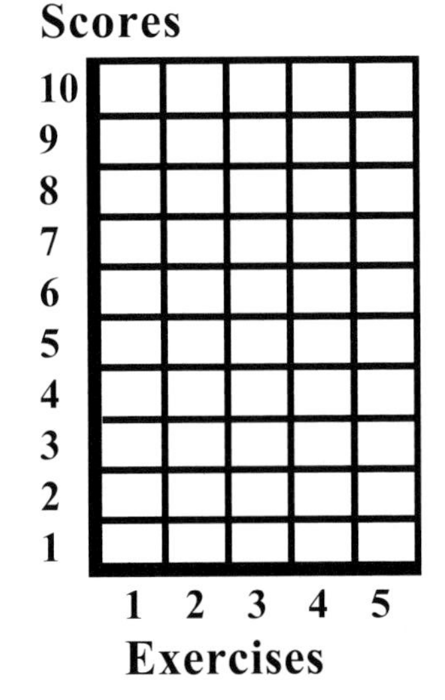

Total Score

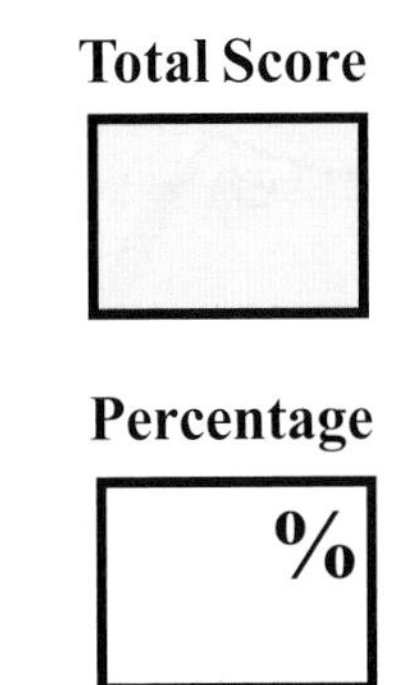

Percentage

%

For the average add up % and divide by 5

Overall Percentage

%

CERTIFICATE OF ACHIEVEMENT (Fourth)

This certifies...................................

has completed ***Maths Book Four*** *successfully.*

Overall Percentage Score Achieved.

%

Comment...................................

...

Signed ....

(teacher/parent/guardian)

Date ....